Study Guide for Essentials of Fire Fighting

Writers

Beth Ann Fulgenzi

Melissa Noakes

Michelle Skidgel

Published by
Fire Protection Publications
Oklahoma State University

RECYCLABLE

The International Fire Service Training Association

The International Fire Service Training Association (IFSTA) was established in 1934 as a "nonprofit educational association of fire fighting personnel who are dedicated to upgrading fire fighting techniques and safety through training." To carry out the mission of IFSTA, Fire Protection Publications was established as an entity of Oklahoma State University. Fire Protection Publications' primary function is to publish and disseminate training texts as proposed and validated by IFSTA. As a secondary function, Fire Protection Publications researches, acquires, produces, and markets high-quality learning and teaching aids consistent with IFSTA's mission.

NOTICE: The questions in this study guide are taken from the information presented in the fifth edition of ***Essentials of Fire Fighting and Fire Department Operations***, an IFSTA-validated manual. The questions are *not validated test questions and are not intended to be duplicated or used for certification or promotional examinations;* this guide is intended to be used as a tool for studying the information presented in ***Essentials of Fire Fighting and Fire Department Operations.***

Copyright © 2008 by the Board of Regents, Oklahoma State University

All rights reserved. No part of this publication may be reproduced in any form without prior written permission from the publisher.

ISBN 9780879392871

First Edition, First Printing, January 2008   *Printed in the United States of America*

10   9   8   7   6   5   4

If you need additional information concerning the International Fire Service Training Association (IFSTA) or Fire Protection Publications, contact:
Customer Service, Fire Protection Publications, Oklahoma State University
930 North Willis, Stillwater, OK 74078-8045
800-654-4055   Fax: 405-744-8204

For assistance with training materials, to recommend material for inclusion in an IFSTA manual, or to ask questions or comment on manual content, contact:
Editorial Department, Fire Protection Publications, Oklahoma State University
930 North Willis, Stillwater, OK 74078-8045
405-744-4111   Fax: 405-744-4112   E-mail: editors@osufpp.org

Oklahoma State University in compliance with Title VI of the Civil Rights Act of 1964 and Title IX of the Educational Amendments of 1972 (Higher Education Act) does not discriminate on the basis of race, color, national origin or sex in any of its policies, practices or procedures. This provision includes but is not limited to admissions, employment, financial aid and educational services.

Table of Contents

Firefighter I Chapters

Firefighter II Chapters

Answers to Chapter Questions

Firefighter I

Firefighter II

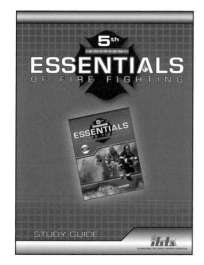

This study guide is designed to help the reader understand and remember the material presented in *Essentials of Fire Fighting and Fire Department Operations*, fifth edition. It identifies important information and concepts from each chapter and provides questions to help the reader study and retain this information. In addition, the study guide serves as an excellent resource for individuals preparing for certification or promotional examinations. The questions in this study guide are divided into Firefighter I and Firefighter II. The questions in this guide are designed to help you remember information and to make you think.

Gratitude is extended to the following members of the Fire Protection Publications staff whose contributions made the final publication of this study guide possible:

Mike Wieder, Assistant Director/Managing Editor
Ed Kirtley, IFSTA/Curriculum Projects Coordinator
Barbara Adams, Senior Editor
Clint Clausing, Senior Editor
Lynne Murnane, Senior Editor
Leslie Miller, Senior Editor
Jeff Fortney, Senior Editor
Carl Goodson, Senior Editor

Ann Moffat, Production Coordinator
Clint Parker, Senior Graphics Designer

Tara Gladden-Graham, Editorial Assistant

Gabriel Ramirez, Research Technician
Mike Sturzenbecker, Graduate Researcher

Chapter 1

Orientation and Fire Service History

Write the correct answers on the blanks provided.

_____ 1. Prior to the early twentieth century, citizens of the Old World and North America were required to keep ____ and containers of water on hand to extinguish any uncontrolled fire. (11)
   A. hoses
   B. buckets of dirt
   C. smothering cloths
   D. a ladder long enough to reach the roof

_____ 2. When did fire fighting tools, equipment, and methods begin to change in North America? (11)
   A. During World War II
   B. During the Civil War
   C. During the Great Depression
   D. During the Industrial Revolution

_____ 3. Which of the following individuals founded the first successful fire insurance company in North America? (12)
   A. Eli Whitney
   B. Joseph Livesey
   C. Benjamin Franklin
   D. Theodore Roosevelt

_____ 4. Various fire insurance companies adopted distinctive symbols, known as ____, and posted one on each property they protected. (12)
   A. insignias
   B. fire marks
   C. flame symbols
   D. proprietary badges

_____ 5. The majority of firefighters in North America are ____ firefighters. (12)
   A. career
   B. federal
   C. volunteer
   D. paid-on-call

_____ 6. From which of the following locations do paid-on-call firefighters usually respond? (13)
   A. The fire station
   B. The police department
   C. Their home or workplace
   D. The nearest military base

_____ 7. Fire departments with ___ personnel primarily protect large towns and cities. (13)
   A. career
   B. military
   C. volunteer
   D. paid-on-call

_____ 8. Promptness, reliability, and initiative are components of: (14)
   A. pride.
   B. courage.
   C. work ethic.
   D. moral character.

_____ 9. Which of the following statements about the definition of an emergency is MOST accurate? (14)
   A. The situation is stabilized.
   B. The situation is improving.
   C. The situation is getting worse.
   D. The situation is getting smaller.

_____ 10. Which of the following BEST describes the mission of the fire service? (15)
   A. To extinguish fires
   B. To promote code compliance
   C. To save lives and protect property
   D. To promote positive public relations

_____ 11. Which of the following tactical priorities keeps a situation from getting worse? (18)
   A. Life safety
   B. Public education
   C. Incident stabilization
   D. Property conservation

_____ 12. Which of the following tactical priorities is always the first and highest priority in any emergency operation? (18)

    A. Life safety

    B. Public education

    C. Incident stabilization

    D. Property conservation

_____ 13. Which of the following organizational principles involves reporting to only one supervisor? (19)

    A. Discipline

    B. Span of control

    C. Division of labor

    D. Unity of command

_____ 14. Which of the following organizational principles means that any officer can effectively manage only a certain number of individuals or groups? (19)

    A. Discipline

    B. Span of control

    C. Division of labor

    D. Unity of command

_____ 15. Which of the following organizational principles is the process of breaking large jobs into smaller jobs to make them more manageable? (20)

    A. Discipline

    B. Span of control

    C. Division of labor

    D. Unity of command

_____ 16. Which of the following organizational principles refers to an organization's responsibility to provide the direction needed to satisfy its identified goals and objectives? (20)

    A. Discipline

    B. Span of control

    C. Division of labor

    D. Unity of command

_____ 17. What is the main purpose of discipline? (21)

    A. To punish

    B. To educate

    C. To rectify wrongdoing

    D. To report inappropriate behavior

_____ 18. Which of the following types of fire companies deploys hoselines for fire attack and exposure protection? (21)

    A. Squad company

    B. Truck company

    C. Engine company

    D. Special rescue company

_____ 19. Which of the following types of fire companies performs forcible entry, search and rescue, ventilation, salvage and overhaul, and utilities control and provides access to upper levels of a structure? (21)

    A. Brush company

    B. Truck company

    C. Rescue squad/company

    D. Emergency medical/ambulance company

_____ 20. Which of the following types of fire companies searches for and removes victims from areas of danger or entrapment? (21)

    A. Engine company

    B. Rescue squad/company

    C. Hazardous materials company

    D. Emergency medical/ambulance company

_____ 21. Which of the following types of fire companies extinguishes wildland fires and protects structures in the wildland/urban interface? (21)

    A. Brush company

    B. Truck company

    C. Special rescue company

    D. Hazardous materials company

_____ 22. Which of the following types of fire companies responds to and mitigates complex hazardous materials incidents? (21)

    A. Truck company

    B. Engine company

    C. Rescue squad/company

    D. Hazardous materials company

_____ 23. Which of the following types of fire companies provides emergency medical care to patients? (21)
   A. Engine company
   B. Ambulance company
   C. Rescue squad/company
   D. Special rescue company

_____ 24. Which of the following types of fire companies would respond to a person trapped in a deep trench cave-in? (21)
   A. Brush company
   B. Truck company
   C. Special rescue company
   D. Rescue squad/company

_____ 25. Which NFPA® professional qualification requirements must a Firefighter I and Firefighter II meet? (24)
   A. NFPA® 1001
   B. NFPA® 1002
   C. NFPA® 1021
   D. NFPA® 1061

_____ 26. Which of the following personnel is ultimately responsible for all operations within the fire department, including obtaining the funds needed to carry out its mission? (26)
   A. Fire chief
   B. Planning officer
   C. Fire administrator
   D. Public information officer

_____ 27. Which of the following personnel monitors operational safety during emergency incidents? (26)
   A. Company officer
   B. Public safety specialist
   C. Public fire and life safety educator
   D. Fire department incident safety officer

_____ 28. Which of the following personnel oversees a fire department's occupational safety and health program? (26)
   A. Public safety specialist
   B. Public fire and life safety educator
   C. Fire department incident safety officer
   D. Fire department health and safety officer

_____ 29. Which of the following personnel receives emergency and nonemergency phone calls and completes incident reports? (27)
   A. Information officer
   B. Public safety specialist
   C. Communications personnel
   D. Information systems personnel

_____ 30. Which of the following personnel assists law enforcement personnel with traffic control, crowd control, and scene security at fires and other emergency operations? (28)
   A. Planning officer
   B. Fire police personnel
   C. Communications personnel
   D. Information systems personnel

_____ 31. Which of the following personnel handles rescue situations such as high-angle (rope) rescue, trench and structural collapse, confined space entry, extrication operations, and cave or mine rescues? (29)
   A. Technical rescuer
   B. Airport firefighter
   C. Fire prevention officer
   D. Emergency medical technician

_____ 32. Which of the following personnel makes presentations and conducts seminars to inform the public about fire hazards, fire causes, precautions, and actions to take during a fire? (30)
   A. Public safety specialist
   B. Fire and arson investigator
   C. Public fire and life safety educator
   D. Fire department incident safety officer

_____ 33. Which of the following personnel stabilizes the victims of accidents or illnesses until more highly trained medical personnel arrive? (30)
   A. Paramedic
   B. First responder
   C. Safety officer
   D. Emergency medical technician

_____ 34. Which of the following personnel provides basic life support (BLS) for the victims of accidents or illnesses but does not provide advanced life support (ALS)? (30)
   A. Paramedic
   B. First responder
   C. Safety officer
   D. Emergency medical technician

35. Which of the following personnel provides advanced life support (ALS) for the victims of accidents and illnesses? (30)

    A. Paramedic
    B. First responder
    C. Safety officer
    D. Emergency medical technician

36. Which of the following terms is defined as "a guide to decision-making within an organization"? (33)

    A. List
    B. Policy
    C. Procedure
    D. Guidebook

37. Which of the following terms is defined as "a written, detailed plan of action"? (33)

    A. List
    B. Policy
    C. Procedure
    D. Guidebook

38. An order is based upon a policy or procedure, whereas a ___ is not. (33)

    A. list
    B. mandate
    C. directive
    D. guidebook

39. Which of the following terms is defined as "standard methods or rules in which an organization or a fire department operates to carry out a routine function"? (33)

    A. Standard Operating Policies
    B. Standard Operating Orders
    C. Standard Operating Methods
    D. Standard Operating Procedures

40. Which of the following systems included in the National Response Plan is the mechanism by which large numbers of fire companies and larger units are organized and managed during emergency incidents? (35)

    A. National Organization System
    B. Standardized System of Planning
    C. Fireground Command Incident System
    D. National Incident Management System

_____ 41. Which of the following statements about a NIMS-compliant Incident Command System is MOST accurate? (35)

    A. Smaller or rural fire departments do not need an Incident Command System.

    B. Whether or not to use an Incident Command System is left up to individual departments.

    C. The requirements for using a NIMS-compliant Incident Command System pertains only to metropolitan fire departments.

    D. All fire departments in the U.S. are required to use a NIMS-compliant Incident Command System.

_____ 42. Which of the following personnel has the authority to call resources to an incident and to release them from it? (36)

    A. Safety Officer

    B. Liaison Officer

    C. Incident Commander

    D. Operations Section Chief

_____ 43. Which of the following personnel serves as the point of contact for other governmental and nongovernmental agencies and private-sector organizations involved in an incident? (36)

    A. Liaison Officer

    B. Planning Section Chief

    C. Public Information Officer

    D. Finance/Administration Section Chief

_____ 44. Which of the following personnel is responsible for the collection, documentation, evaluation, and dissemination of incident situation information and intelligence to the Incident Commander? (37)

    A. Logistics Section Chief

    B. Planning Section Chief

    C. Public Information Officer

    D. Finance/Administration Section Chief

_____ 45. Which of the following personnel is responsible for all support requirements needed to facilitate effective and efficient incident management? (37)

    A. Logistics Section Chief

    B. Planning Section Chief

    C. Operations Section Chief

    D. Information/Intelligence Section Chief

_____ 46. Which of the following ICS terms is used to describe resources that have checked in at the incident and are not currently assigned? (39)

A. Assigned

B. Available

C. Out-of-Service

D. Resource Status

_____ 47. Which of the following ICS terms is used to describe the organizational level between Divisions/Groups and the IC and Operations? (39)

A. Branch

B. Level II

C. Division

D. Command

_____ 48. Which of the following ICS terms is used to describe a geographic designation assigning responsibility for all operations within a defined area? (39)

A. Branch

B. Group

C. Division

D. Command

_____ 49. Which of the following ICS terms is used to describe the written or unwritten plan for managing the emergency? (39)

A. Incident Preplan

B. Incident Action Plan

C. Incident Analysis

D. Command Guidebook

_____ 50. Which of the following ICS terms is used to describe all personnel and major pieces of apparatus on scene or en route and on which status is maintained? (40)

A. Kit

B. Staff

C. Inventory

D. Resources

_____ 51. Which of the following is one of the three status modes assigned to resources at a particular incident? (40)

A. Ready

B. Waiting

C. Assigned

D. In-service

_____ 52. Which of the following ICS terms is used to describe any combination of resources assembled in support of a specific mission or operational need? (40)

A. Task Force

B. Strike Team

C. Resource Status

D. Rapid Intervention Crew

_____ 53. Which of the following ICS terms is defined as "set number or resources of the same kind and type with an established minimum number of personnel"? (40)

A. Group

B. Division

C. Task Force

D. Strike Team

_____ 54. Which of the following statements about the Command Post is MOST accurate? (39)

A. There is only one Command Post per incident.

B. There can be multiple Command Posts per incident.

C. There should be no more than two separate Command Posts per incident.

D. There should be no more than three separate Command Posts per incident.

_____ 55. Upon which of the following does the level of first-aid training by firefighters depend, in addition to the department's SOPs? (40)

A. The local EMS system

B. The size of the jurisdiction

C. The local hospital's capabilities

D. The population of the jurisdiction

_____ 56. In which of the following emergency situations are hospital personnel MOST likely to be called to the scene? (41)

A. A one-car wreck

B. A single house fire

C. A suicide attempt

D. A passenger train accident

_____ 57. What is the priority of law enforcement personnel present at a fire scene? (42)

A. Scene security

B. Extricating victims

C. Overhauling the scene

D. Driving the apparatus

_____ 58. Which of the following organizations is MOST likely to have specially trained and equipped emergency response teams? (42)

A.   Utility company

B.   Law enforcement

C.   Environmental Protection Agency

D.   Medical examiner's office

_____ 59. As a firefighter, you should NOT make comments or express opinions to members of the media but should direct them to: (43)

A.   the fire chief.

B.   the Incident Commander.

C.   union representatives.

D.   the Public Information Officer.

_____ 60. Which of the following organizations can be helpful in alerting the public when large-scale evacuations are necessary? (43)

A.   News media

B.   Hospital

C.   Law enforcement

D.   Utility company

1. According to statistics compiled by the U.S. Fire Administration (USFA), how many firefighter injuries are reported on average in the U.S. each year? (50)
    A. 50,000
    B. 75,000
    C. 100,000
    D. 125,000

2. Which of the following actions is an effective way to prevent firefighter injuries? (50)
    A. Limit physical activities performed.
    B. Allow firefighters to freelance at incidents.
    C. Work with as few personnel as possible.
    D. Maintain company discipline and accountability.

3. Rules, principles, or measures that are established through agreement of members of a standards-setting organization such as NFPA® are called: (52)
    A. regulations.
    B. consensus standards.
    C. regulatory commitments.
    D. required standard procedures.

4. Which of the following statements about National Fire Protection Association standards is MOST accurate? (52)
    A. They are only guidelines and are not adopted as laws.
    B. They are automatically considered law in the U.S. and Canada.
    C. They are not law unless adopted by a state, provincial, or local governing body.
    D. All governing bodies in the U.S. and Canada must adopt applicable standards into law.

5. Which of the following NFPA® standards is the most comprehensive standard relating to firefighter safety and health? (52)
    A. NFPA® 1001
    B. NFPA® 1500
    C. NFPA® 1982
    D. NFPA® 2001

_____ 6. Which of the following documents is a written plan that identifies and analyzes the exposure to hazards? (52)

A. Safety policy

B. Hazard guideline

C. Risk management plan

D. Exposure and hazard report

_____ 7. Who is assigned and authorized by the fire and emergency services administration as the manager of the health and safety program? (53)

A. Fire Chief

B. Company Officer

C. Health and Safety Officer

D. Firefighter Health Manager

_____ 8. Which of the following situations is NOT an exception for the rule that personnel riding in the apparatus be seated and securely belted inside the cab or body of the vehicle whenever it is in motion? (53)

A. Hose loading

B. Tiller training

C. Haz mat response

D. Some EMS operations

_____ 9. Which of the following is a respirator worn by the user that supplies a breathable atmosphere that is either carried in or generated by the apparatus? (53)

A. Air mask

B. Supplied-air respirator

C. Personal alert safety system

D. Self-contained breathing apparatus

_____ 10. Which of the following is a medical requirement of NFPA® 1500? (55)

A. Annual medical verification of continued fitness for duty

B. Abstinence of any alcohol or tobacco products both on and off duty

C. Verification that member has never filed any workers' compensation claims

D. Verification that member does not engage in any dangerous sport activities off duty

_____ 11. Which of the following is a duty for employers according to the Occupational Safety and Health Administration (OSHA)? (56)

A. Protect the environment.

B. Write firefighter professional qualification requirements.

C. Prevent firefighter injuries and deaths through education.

D. Furnish employees a place of employment free from recognized hazards.

_____ 12. Which of the following terms describes a team of employees organized within a private company who are assigned to respond to fires and emergencies on that property? (56)

    A. Volunteer crew

    B. Industrial fire brigade

    C. Firefighter employee team

    D. Private property protection unit

_____ 13. Federal OSHA regulations apply: (56)

    A. to all firefighters.

    B. only to local and state public-sector firefighters.

    C. only to federal employees who fight fires on federal property.

    D. only to federal employees and private-sector employees who fight fires.

_____ 14. According to the IFSTA Principles of Risk Management, no risk to the safety of members shall be acceptable when: (58)

    A. there is no possibility to save lives or property.

    B. a defensive attack has been selected and is being used.

    C. there are no back-up personnel available if injuries occur.

    D. individuals needing assistance have placed themselves in the situation.

_____ 15. Which of the following is the highest fireground priority? (58)

    A. Extinguishing the fire

    B. Determining the cause of the fire

    C. Minimizing damage to surrounding structures

    D. Protecting your life and those of your fellow firefighters

_____ 16. Which of the following is NOT a main goal of a safety program? (59)

    A. Preventing damage to or loss of equipment

    B. Preventing human suffering, deaths, injuries, and illnesses

    C. Reducing the ill effects of publicity regarding unsafe acts by firefighters

    D. Reducing the incidence and severity of accidents and hazardous exposures

_____ 17. To maintain your personal health as a firefighter, follow recommendations for vaccinations against: (60)

    A. hepatitis A.

    B. hepatitis B.

    C. tuberculosis.

    D. HIV/AIDS.

_____ 18. To maintain your personal health as a firefighter, maintain a diet: (61)

   A. low in cholesterol, fat, and sodium.

   B. high in cholesterol, fat, and sodium.

   C. low in cholesterol and high in fat and sodium.

   D. high in cholesterol and low in fat and sodium.

_____ 19. Which of the following terms describes pathogenic microorganisms that are present in the human blood and can cause disease in humans? (61)

   A. Chemical hazards

   B. Airborne pathogens

   C. Bloodborne pathogens

   D. Hazardous waste pathogens

_____ 20. Which of the following programs would help a firefighter who is dealing with financial problems? (61)

   A. Union program

   B. Wellness program

   C. Aid and assistance regimen

   D. Employee assistance program

_____ 21. Which of the following programs would help a firefighter who wanted to lose weight? (61)

   A. Union program

   B. Wellness program

   C. Aid and assistance regimen

   D. Employee assistance program

_____ 22. Any employee assistance programs provided for departmental personnel: (62)

   A. should also be made available to family members.

   B. should be made available to family members for a fee.

   C. are not available to anyone not directly employed by the department.

   D. should be made available to employees after 1 year of employment.

_____ 23. When should the process of managing stress related to a fire scene begin? (62)

   A. During rehab

   B. After the incident is terminated

   C. After firefighters leave the scene

   D. Before firefighters enter the scene

_____ 24. In most departments, which of the following must firefighters wear when they enter the cab of the apparatus? (63)

    A. SCBA

    B. PASS device

    C. Station clothing

    D. All of their protective clothing

_____ 25. Which of the following is one exception to the use of handrails when dismounting an apparatus? (64)

    A. When not wearing SCBA

    B. When the company officer permits

    C. When the need to dismount quickly is present

    D. When the apparatus is close to electrical wires

_____ 26. Who is responsible for visitors while they are in the fire department building? (65)

    A. The fire department

    B. The police department

    C. The individual who requested the tour

    D. Visitors are responsible for themselves

_____ 27. Which of the following is the most common injury related to improper lifting and carrying? (65)

    A. Knee strains

    B. Back strains

    C. Arm injuries

    D. Lower leg injuries

_____ 28. Which of the following is a proper procedure when using hand and power tools? (66)

    A. Wear comfortable, loose clothing.

    B. Use badly worn tools with extra caution.

    C. Modify tools as necessary for ease of use.

    D. Wear appropriate personal protective equipment.

_____ 29. Who should be allowed to use power tools? (66)

    A. All fire department personnel

    B. Only firefighters in a supervisory position

    C. Only those firefighters who have read and who understand the tool manufacturer's instructions

    D. Firefighters with a background in using power tools who enjoy working with tools

_____ 30. Which of the following statements about preventing accidents when using power saws is MOST accurate? (67)

  A. Wear comfortable, loose clothing.

  B. Keep bystanders out of the work area.

  C. Refuel gasoline-powered saws while still warm.

  D. Use power saws as necessary in potentially flammable atmospheres.

_____ 31. Which of the following NFPA® standards gives the requirements for conducting live fire training? (68)

  A. NFPA® 1403

  B. NFPA® 1500

  C. NFPA® 1971

  D. NFPA® 1982

_____ 32. A training structure specially designed to contain live fires for the purpose of fire-suppression training is known as a: (68)

  A. fire house.

  B. burn building.

  C. heat-resistant structure.

  D. evolution performance zone.

_____ 33. When conducting live fire training, a student-to-instructor ratio of ___ may not be exceeded. (68)

  A. 5:1

  B. 6:1

  C. 7:1

  D. 8:1

_____ 34. When conducting live fire training, fires may not be set: (68)

  A. in attics.

  B. in egress routes.

  C. inside the building.

  D. outside the building.

_____ 35. At the beginning of every work shift, you should ensure that your SCBA is fully functional and: (70)

  A. has an air cylinder at least 50% full.

  B. has an air cylinder at least 60% full.

  C. has an air cylinder at least 75% full.

  D. has a full air cylinder.

_____ 36. Which of the following is the LEAST likely to be considered a critical factor during size-up by the Incident Commander? (70)
   A. Presence of news media
   B. Life safety hazards
   C. Nature and extent of the emergency
   D. Building type, arrangement, and access

_____ 37. Which of the following types of operations is conducted inside the hazard zone? (70)
   A. Neutral operations
   B. Offensive operations
   C. Defensive operations
   D. Scene control operations

_____ 38. Which of the following types of operations is conducted outside the hazard zone? (70)
   A. Neutral operations
   B. Offensive operations
   C. Defensive operations
   D. Hazardous operations

_____ 39. Which of the following signifies that companies working in the hazard zone are all safe and accounted for? (71)
   A. Safety Log
   B. Personnel Log
   C. Incident Action Report
   D. Personnel Accountability Report

_____ 40. Which of the following signals signifies that the primary search has been completed and all savable occupants are out of the hazard zone? (71)
   A. All Clear
   B. Loss Stopped
   C. Under Control
   D. Out of Danger

_____ 41. Which of the following signals signifies that the forward progress of the fire has been stopped? (71)
   A. All Clear
   B. Loss Stopped
   C. Under Control
   D. Out of Danger

_____ 42. All companies working in the hazard zone must be assigned according to the fireground organizational structure and must work: (71)

  A. within the Incident Action Plan.

  B. with a minimum amount of freelancing.

  C. outside of the collapse zone of the structure.

  D. following SOPs that they feel are appropriate.

_____ 43. Which of the following actions should occur after a primary _All Clear_ and the _Under Control_ benchmarks have been completed? (71)

  A. All efforts must be focused on recovering victims.

  B. All efforts must be focused on investigating the fire.

  C. All efforts must be focused on making incident reports.

  D. All efforts must be focused on controlling the loss to the structure and its contents.

_____ 44. Two or more fully equipped and immediately available firefighters who are designated to stand by outside the hazard zone to enter and effect rescue of firefighters inside if necessary are known as a(n): (72)

  A. tag team.

  B. first responder crew.

  C. rapid intervention crew (RIC).

  D. emergency firefighter rescue team.

_____ 45. Which of the following is the name of the guidelines for operating at highway emergencies published by the U.S. Department of Transportation (DOT)? (72)

  A. _Emergency Response Guidebook_

  B. _Principles of Vehicle Extrication_

  C. _Highway Emergency Guidebook_

  D. _Manual of Uniform Traffic Control Devices_

_____ 46. How many traffic lanes next to an emergency incident should be closed? (73)

  A. None

  B. At least one

  C. At least two

  D. All traffic lanes

_____ 47. Which of the following usually has responsibility for crowd control at an incident? (74)

  A. Media personnel

  B. Fire department personnel

  C. Law enforcement personnel

  D. Private security guards

_____ 48. What are the most common designations for control zones? (74)

   A. Hot, warm, and cold

   B. Area 1, Area 2, and Area 3

   C. Safe, dangerous, and hazardous

   D. Primary, secondary, and tertiary

_____ 49. Every fire department must use some system of accountability that identifies and tracks all personnel: (74)

   A. at the fire station.

   B. riding on apparatus.

   C. while both on and off duty.

   D. working in the hazard zone at an incident.

_____ 50. What is another name for a passport system that can aid in accounting for personnel within the hazard zone? (75)

   A. Tag system

   B. PASS system

   C. Hazard system

   D. Identification system

_____ 51. Which of the following is a technique for interior fire fighting operations? (76-77)

   A. Focus only on what is immediately in front of you.

   B. Separate from your team once inside the building.

   C. Limit tools and equipment taken in the building.

   D. Wear full PPE including SCBA and use an air management plan.

_____ 52. If you find yourself separated from your company and trapped in a burning building, you need to call for help: (77)

   A. immediately.

   B. after 3-5 minutes.

   C. after 5-7 minutes.

   D. after exhausting all other options.

_____ 53. Which of the following terms refers to an international distress signal broadcast by voice? (77)

   A. SOS

   B. Mayday

   C. Emergency help

   D. Voice alert

_____ 54. Which of the following situations is the MOST likely to require emergency escape? (77)

A. Water rescue

B. Vehicle fire

C. Structural collapse

D. Hazardous materials release

_____ 55. Which of the following statements about rapid intervention crews (RICs) is MOST accurate? (78)

A. RIC members cannot be assigned other fireground support duties.

B. Being part of a RIC is a secondary assignment and other duties take precedence.

C. The primary job of a RIC is to help firefighters with Rehab once they are outside of the building.

D. RIC members may be assigned other fireground support duties as long as they can fulfill their primary function.

_____ 1. What is anything that occupies space and has mass? (87)
- A. Matter
- B. Substance
- C. Component
- D. Spatial mass

_____ 2. What is a chemical reaction between two or more materials that changes the materials and produces heat, flames, and toxic smoke? (87)
- A. Boiling reaction
- B. Spontaneous reaction
- C. Exothermic heat reaction
- D. Endothermic heat reaction

_____ 3. What is a chemical reaction in which a substance absorbs heat energy? (87)
- A. Oxidation reaction
- B. Combustion reaction
- C. Exothermic heat reaction
- D. Endothermic heat reaction

_____ 4. What is an exothermic chemical reaction called that releases energy in the form of heat and sometimes light? (87)
- A. Inertia
- B. Oxidation
- C. Combustion
- D. Flammability

_____ 5. How are modes of combustion differentiated? (87)
- A. Based on the length of the reaction
- B. Based on the temperature of the reaction
- C. Based on when the reaction is occurring
- D. Based on where the reaction is occurring

_____ 6. Which of the following is NOT a component of the fire triangle? (87)
- A. Fuel
- B. Heat
- C. Oxygen
- D. Accelerant

Firefighter I

_____ 7. Which of the following is NOT a component of the fire tetrahedron? (87-88)

    A. Heat

    B. Oxygen

    C. High-heat accelerant

    D. Self-sustained chemical chain reaction

_____ 8. Energy possessed by an object that may be released in the future is known as: (89)

    A. still energy.

    B. stored energy.

    C. kinetic energy.

    D. potential energy.

_____ 9. Which of the following types of energy is the energy possessed by a moving object? (89)

    A. Used energy

    B. Kinetic energy

    C. Moving energy

    D. Potential energy

_____ 10. The capacity to perform work is known as: (89)

    A. ability.

    B. energy.

    C. movability.

    D. motivation.

_____ 11. Which of the following is the measure for heat energy in the International System of Units? (89)

    A. Joule

    B. Degree

    C. Newton

    D. British thermal unit

_____ 12. Which of the following is the measure for heat energy in the customary system? (89)

    A. Joule

    B. Degree

    C. Newton

    D. British thermal unit

_____ 13. The chemical decomposition of a substance through the action of heat is known as: (90)

   A. flame.

   B. pyrolysis.

   C. flammability.

   D. stabilization.

_____ 14. Which of the following is one of the two forms of ignition? (90)

   A. Nonignition

   B. Autoignition

   C. Microignition

   D. Complete ignition

_____ 15. What is the temperature to which the surface of a substance must be heated for ignition and self-sustained combustion to occur? (90-91)

   A. Autoignition temperature

   B. Combustion temperature

   C. Flammability temperature

   D. Microignition temperature

_____ 16. Which of the following is the most common source of heat in combustion reactions? (91)

   A. Sound energy

   B. Nuclear energy

   C. Chemical heat energy

   D. Mechanical heat energy

_____ 17. What is a form of chemical heat energy that occurs when a material increases in temperature without the addition of external heat? (91)

   A. Self-heating

   B. Internal-heating

   C. Chemically-heating

   D. Carbonation-heating

_____ 18. What happens to the rate of the oxidation reaction as more heat is generated and held by the materials insulating the fuel? (92)

   A. It increases.

   B. It decreases.

   C. It stays the same.

   D. It ceases completely.

_____ 19. Which of the following types of energy is generated by friction or compression? (93)
A. Light energy
B. Sound energy
C. Chemical heat energy
D. Mechanical heat energy

_____ 20. Which of the following is the transfer of heat within a body or to another body by direct contact? (94)
A. Transfer
B. Radiation
C. Convection
D. Conduction

_____ 21. Which of the following is the transfer of heat energy from a fluid to a solid surface? (95)
A. Transfer
B. Radiation
C. Convection
D. Conduction

_____ 22. Which of the following is the transmission of energy as an electromagnetic wave? (95)
A. Transfer
B. Radiation
C. Convection
D. Conduction

_____ 23. Which of the following is a material that absorbs heat but does not participate actively in the combustion reaction? (96)
A. Passive agent
B. Inactive agent
C. Retardant agent
D. Inflammable agent

_____ 24. The material or substance being oxidized or burned in the combustion process is known as: (96)
A. fuel.
B. flame.
C. accelerant.
D. oxidizing agent.

25. Gases with a vapor density of less than 1 will: (97)
  A. rise.
  B. sink.
  C. freeze.
  D. boil.

26. Which of the following is the ratio of the mass of a given volume of a liquid compared with the mass of an equal volume of water at the same temperature? (97)
  A. Mass ratio
  B. Equality scale
  C. Specific gravity
  D. Temperate volume

27. What is the transformation of a liquid to vapor or gaseous state? (97)
  A. Oxidation
  B. Gaseousity
  C. Vaporization
  D. Liquidization

28. What is the temperature at which a liquid gives off sufficient vapors to ignite, but not sustain, combustion? (98)
  A. Fire point
  B. Flash point
  C. Flame point
  D. Ignition level

29. What is the temperature at which sufficient vapors are being generated to sustain the combustion reaction? (98)
  A. Fire point
  B. Flash point
  C. Flame point
  D. Combustion level

30. Which of the following terms describes the extent to which a substance will mix with water? (99)
  A. Liquidity
  B. Solubility
  C. Potability
  D. Proportionality

_____ 31. Materials that will mix in any proportion in water are: (99)

A. soluble.

B. miscible.

C. dissolvable.

D. proportional.

_____ 32. The surface area of a fuel in proportion to its mass is called: (101)

A. area proportion.

B. mass proportionality.

C. surface-to-mass ratio.

D. surface-area proportion.

_____ 33. What is the total amount of energy released when a specific amount of a given fuel is oxidized? (102)

A. Heat energy

B. Heat release rate

C. Heat of combustion

D. Fuel oxidation number

_____ 34. What is the energy released per unit of time as a given fuel burns? (103)

A. Heat energy

B. Heat release rate

C. Rate of combustion

D. Fuel oxidation number

_____ 35. What is known as the range of concentrations of the fuel vapor and air? (105)

A. Heat range

B. Flammable range

C. Lower flammable limit

D. Upper flammable limit

_____ 36. Exposure to which of the following substances is frequently identified as the cause of death for civilian fire fatalities? (108)

A. Methane

B. Carbon dioxide

C. Carbon monoxide

D. Hydrogen cyanide

_____ 37. Which of the following substances acts to prevent the body from using oxygen at the cellular level and is a byproduct of the combustion of polyurethane foam? (108)

A. Carbon dioxide

B. Carbon monoxide

C. Hydrogen cyanide

D. Hydrogen peroxide

_____ 38. Which of the following substances is a product of complete combustion of organic materials and acts as a simple asphyxiant by displacing oxygen? (108)

A. Methane

B. Carbon dioxide

C. Carbon monoxide

D. Hydrogen cyanide

_____ 39. Which of the following substances is a colorless liquid with a pungent choking odor, and is irritating to the mucous membranes? (109)

A. Benzene

B. Acetaldehyde

C. Sulfur dioxide

D. Hydrogen chloride

_____ 40. Which of the following substances is a colorless-to-clear yellow liquid with a bitter almond odor? (109)

A. Asbestos

B. Particulates

C. Benzaldehyde

D. Glutaraldehyde

_____ 41. Which of the following substances is a colorless liquid with a weak, suffocating odor? (109)

A. Acrolein

B. Formaldehyde

C. Nitrogen dioxide

D. Isovaleraldehyde

_____ 42. Which of the following types of fire involve flammable and combustible liquids and gases? (110)

A. Class B

B. Class C

C. Class D

D. Class K

_____ 43. Which of the following types of fire involve ordinary combustible materials? (110)
- A. Class A
- B. Class B
- C. Class C
- D. Class D

_____ 44. Which of the following types of fire involve energized electrical equipment? (110-111)
- A. Class A
- B. Class B
- C. Class C
- D. Class K

_____ 45. Which of the following types of fire involve combustible metals? (111)
- A. Class B
- B. Class C
- C. Class D
- D. Class K

_____ 46. Which of the following types of fire involve oils and greases normally found in commercial kitchens? (112)
- A. Class A
- B. Class B
- C. Class C
- D. Class K

_____ 47. When sufficient oxygen is available and fire development is controlled by the characteristics and configuration of the fuel, it is said to be: (113)
- A. uncontrolled.
- B. fuel controlled.
- C. oxygen controlled.
- D. combustible controlled.

_____ 48. The first stage of the burning process in a confined space in which the substance being oxidized is producing some heat, but the heat has not spread to other substances nearby, is known as: (114)
- A. the decay stage.
- B. the growth stage.
- C. the incipient stage.
- D. the fully developed stage.

_____ 49. Which of the following types of ignition is caused when a material reaches its autoignition temperature as the result of self-heating? (114)
   A. Heated
   B. Piloted
   C. Automatic
   D. Nonpiloted

_____ 50. Mushrooming, in scientific terms, is known as a: (114)
   A. ceiling jet.
   B. gas balloon.
   C. smoke fungus.
   D. toxic fume cloud.

_____ 51. Thermal layering of gases is the tendency of gases to form into layers according to temperature and is also known as: (117)
   A. heat stratification.
   B. temperate balance.
   C. cool-heat layering.
   D. neutral plane balance.

_____ 52. Pockets of flames may be observed moving through the hot gas layer above the neutral plane, a phenomenon known as: (118)
   A. flaming.
   B. ghosting.
   C. heat layering.
   D. neutral plane pocketing.

_____ 53. A condition where the unburned fire gases accumulated at the top of the compartment ignite and flames propagate through the hot gas layer or across the ceiling is: (118)
   A. rollover.
   B. flashover.
   C. isolated flames.
   D. thermal layering.

_____ 54. Which of the following terms describes when the temperature in a compartment results in the simultaneous ignition of all of the combustible contents in the space? (120)
   A. Rollover
   B. Flashover
   C. Isolated flames
   D. Thermal layering

_____ 55. The fire stage that occurs when all combustible materials in the compartment are burning is known as the: (121)

    A. decay stage.

    B. growth stage.

    C. incipient stage.

    D. fully developed stage.

_____ 56. The fire stage in which the oxygen concentration falls to the point where flaming combustion can no longer be supported is known as the: (121)

    A. decay stage.

    B. growth stage.

    C. incipient stage.

    D. fully developed stage.

_____ 57. An increase in ventilation can result in a deflagration called: (122)

    A. rollover.

    B. flashover.

    C. foredraft.

    D. backdraft.

_____ 58. Which of the following are the most fundamental fuel characteristics influencing fire development in a compartment? (125)

    A. Volume and mass

    B. Mass and surface area

    C. Weight and surface area

    D. Perimeter, mass, and volume

_____ 59. All other things being equal, how will a fire in a large compartment develop compared to one in a small compartment? (127)

    A. More slowly

    B. More quickly

    C. More intensely

    D. More dangerously

_____ 60. Which of the following is one of the most common methods of fire control and extinguishment? (130)

    A. Cooling with water

    B. Smothering with foam

    C. Setting a secondary fire

    D. Dousing with chemical extinguishing agents

_____ 61. When does water have its greatest effect on a fire? (131)
   A. As it is applied to the fire
   B. As its temperature is raised
   C. As it is vaporized into steam
   D. As it cools the structure after the fire

_____ 62. Which of the following is the preferred method of extinguishing pressurized gas fires? (131)
   A. Smothering with foam
   B. Extinguishing with water
   C. Allowing the fire to burn until all fuel is consumed
   D. Stopping the flow of liquid or gaseous fuel by closing a valve

_____ 63. Which of the following methods is used to extinguish rangetop fires when a cover is placed on a pan of burning grease? (131)
   A. Fuel removal
   B. Oxygen exclusion
   C. Temperature reduction
   D. Chemical flame inhibition

_____ 1. Two or more interconnected structural components combined to meet a specific function or design requirement is known as a(n): (138-140)

   A. sheath.

   B. course.

   C. assembly.

   D. platform construction.

_____ 2. Which of the following is a horizontal structural component subjected to vertical loads? (138-140)

   A. Beam

   B. Column

   C. Parapet

   D. Gusset plate

_____ 3. Which of the following is an open space between the roof and ceiling of a commercial or industrial building? (138-140)

   A. Stud

   B. Girder

   C. Cockloft

   D. Cantilever

_____ 4. Which of the following is a nonload-bearing interior wall extending down from a roof or ceiling to limit the horizontal spread of fire and heat? (138-140)

   A. Decking

   B. Party wall

   C. Gusset plate

   D. Curtain board

_____ 5. Which of the following is the total potential heat release if a building and its contents burned? (138-140)

   A. Tension

   B. Fire load

   C. Rated assembly

   D. Interstitial space

_____ 6. Which of the following is a pitched roof characterized by square-cut ends and sides that slope down from the ridge line to the eaves? (138-140)

    A. Hip roof

    B. Gable roof

    C. Gambrel roof

    D. Mansard roof

_____ 7. Which of the following is a wooden structural member composed of relatively short pieces of lumber glued and laminated together under pressure to form a long, extremely strong beam? (138-140)

    A. Joist

    B. Column

    C. Glue-lam beam

    D. Header course

_____ 8. Which of the following is a roof characterized by steeply sloped facets surrounding a flat or nearly flat center section? (138-140)

    A. Hip roof

    B. Flat roof

    C. Gambrel roof

    D. Mansard roof

_____ 9. Which of the following is a mixture of sand, cement, and water used to bond masonry units into a solid mass? (138-140)

    A. Pitch

    B. Rebar

    C. Mortar

    D. Drywall

_____ 10. Which of the following is a wooden structural panel formed by gluing and compressing wood strands together under pressure? (138-140)

    A. Chipboard

    B. Curtain board

    C. Gypsum board

    D. Oriented strand board

_____ 11. Which of the following is the ratio of rise-to-span of a roof assembly? (138-140)

    A. Pitch

    B. Tension

    C. Spalling

    D. Assembly

_____ 12. Which of the following is the top or bottom horizontal member of a frame wall? (138-140)

A. Stud

B. Plate

C. Beam

D. Column

_____ 13. Which of the following are beams that span from a ridge board to an exterior wall plate to support roof decking? (138-140)

A. Rebar

B. Rafters

C. Cantilevers

D. Lamella arches

_____ 14. Which of the following is plywood, OSB, or wooden planking applied to a wall or roof over which a weather-resistant covering is applied? (138-140)

A. Truss

B. Parapet

C. Bar joist

D. Sheathing

_____ 15. Which of the following is degradation to concrete due to prolonged exposure to high heat? (138-140)

A. Spalling

B. Decking

C. Sheathing

D. Compression

_____ 16. Which of the following is a type of wood-frame construction in which the studs in exterior walls extend from the basement or foundation to the roof? (138-140)

A. Balloon frame

B. Rated assembly

C. Open web joist

D. Platform construction

_____ 17. Which of the following is a horizontal structural member used to support beams or joists? (138-140)

A. Eave

B. Rebar

C. Girder

D. Lamella arches

_____ 18. Which of the following is a pitched roof that slopes in one direction only from the ridge? (138-140)

A. Parapet

B. Cockloft

C. Shed roof

D. Mansard roof

_____ 19. Which of the following is a pitched roof in which the ends are all beveled so there are no gable walls? (138-140)

A. Hip roof

B. Shed roof

C. Gambrel roof

D. Butterfly roof

_____ 20. Which of the following is the main structural members of a truss as distinguished from diagonals? (138-140)

A. Chord

B. Bar joist

C Cantilever

D. Header course

_____ 21. Which of the following is the most common building material used in North America? (141)

A. Wood

B. Concrete

C. Cast iron

D. Fiberglass

_____ 22. Because masonry materials do not burn, a variety of masonry walls are used in the construction of: (142)

A. homes.

B. fire walls.

C. curtain walls.

D. apartment buildings.

_____ 23. Which of the following materials was commonly used as an exterior surface covering and is typically found only on older buildings? (143)

A. Steel

B. Gypsum

C. Cast iron

D. Fiberglass

_____ 24. Which of the following is the primary material used for structural support in the construction of large modern buildings? (143)
A. Steel
B. Glass
C. Wood
D. Concrete

_____ 25. Which of the following has the compressive strength of concrete along with the tensile strength of steel? (144)
A. Glass
B. Masonry
C. Cast iron
D. Reinforced concrete

_____ 26. Which of the following is an inorganic product from which plaster and wallboards are constructed? (145)
A. Gypsum
B. Masonry
C. Cast iron
D. Fiberglass

_____ 27. Which of the following is primarily used for insulation purposes? (145)
A. Steel
B. Wood
C. Gypsum
D. Fiberglass

_____ 28. Which of the following types of construction is known as *fire-resistive construction*? (146)
A. Type I
B. Type II
C. Type III
D. Type IV

_____ 29. Which of the following types of construction is commonly used to construct the typical single-family residence or apartment house of up to seven stories? (149)
A. Type I
B. Type II
C. Type IV
D. Type V

_____ 30. Which of the following types of construction is known as *heavy-timber construction*? (148)

A. Type I

B. Type II

C. Type III

D. Type IV

_____ 31. Which of the following types of construction resists collapse due to flame impingement of heavy beams? (149)

A. Type I

B. Type II

C. Type IV

D. Type V

_____ 32. Which of the following types of construction confines fire well and is impervious to water damage but is difficult to breach for access or escape? (146)

A. Type I

B. Type III

C. Type IV

D. Type V

_____ 33. Which of the following types of construction is known as *noncombustible construction*? (147)

A. Type I

B. Type II

C. Type III

D. Type IV

_____ 34. Which of the following types of construction resists fire spread from the outside but is susceptible to water damage? (148)

A. Type II

B. Type III

C. Type IV

D. Type V

_____ 35. Which of the following types of construction is known as ordinary construction? (148)

A. Type I

B. Type II

C. Type III

D. Type IV

_____ 36. Which of the following types of construction is resistant to collapse from earthquakes due to light weight and flexibility? (149-150)

A. Type I

B. Type III

C. Type IV

D. Type V

_____ 37. The presence of large amounts of combustible materials in an area or a building is known as: (152)

A. overloading.

B. irresponsible.

C. heavy fire loading.

D. danger zone material.

_____ 38. Historically, which of the following roofing materials contributes MOST to fire spread? (153)

A. Tin

B. Tar

C. Slate

D. Wood shakes

_____ 39. Proper use of which of the following is considered MOST necessary for slowing the spread of fire in large, open spaces? (153)

A. Forced ventilation

B. Vertical ventilation

C. Hydraulic ventilation

D. Horizontal ventilation

_____ 40. Buildings of truss construction will succumb to the effects of fire ___ than a heavy timber building. (154)

A. much slower

B. much quicker

C. a little slower

D. a little quicker

_____ 41. Which of the following terms BEST describes the area extending horizontally from the base of the wall to one and one-half times the height of the wall? (154)

A. Hot zone

B. Cold zone

C. Warm zone

D. Collapse zone

_____ 42. Which of the following is NOT an indicator of pending building collapse? (155-156)

    A. Walls that appear to be leaning

    B. Smoke coming from windows and doors

    C. Structural members pulling away from walls

    D. Fires beneath floors that support heavy machinery or other extreme weight loads

_____ 43. Which of the following techniques can result in structural supports being cut that could weaken the structure? (156)

    A. Improper vertical ventilation

    B. Improper horizontal ventilation

    C. Improper positive-pressure ventilation

    D. Improper negative-pressure ventilation

_____ 44. Which of the following is the FIRST step that should be taken if building collapse is suspected? (156)

    A. Establish a collapse zone.

    B. Inform Command of the situation.

    C. Cautiously place master stream devices.

    D. Immediately withdraw master stream devices.

_____ 45. Which of the following is one of the most common types of lightweight construction? (156)

    A. Gypsum trusses

    B. Fiberglass trusses

    C. Lightweight steel trusses

    D. Lightweight concrete trusses

_____ 46. One of the most common types of lightweight construction is: (156)

    A. masonry trusses.

    B. compression trusses.

    C. lightweight gusset trusses.

    D. lightweight wooden trusses.

_____ 47. Gusset plates may be wooden or: (156)

    A. glass.

    B. metal.

    C. concrete.

    D. fiberglass.

48. Unprotected lightweight steel and wooden trusses can fail after how many minutes of exposure to fire? (156)

    A. 5 to 10
    B. 10 to 15
    C. 15 to 20
    D. 20 to 25

49. At which of the following temperatures do steel trusses begin to fail? (156)

    A. 750°F (400°C)
    B. 1,000°F (538°C)
    C. 1,250°F (677°C)
    D. 1,500°F (815°C)

50. In which of the following buildings would bowstring trusses MOST likely be found? (157-158)

    A. Two-story home
    B. Convenience store
    C. Apartment building
    D. Automobile dealership

51. When is the presence of bowstring trusses BEST identified? (158)

    A. During size-up
    B. During the investigation
    C. During firefighting operations
    D. During preincident planning surveys

Firefighter I

_____ 1. One main factor affecting the reaction of wood to fire conditions is the: (142)
    A. size of the wood.
    B. grain of the wood.
    C. color of the wood.
    D. strength of the wood.

_____ 2. A main factor affecting the reaction of wood to fire conditions is: (142)
    A. its hardness.
    B. its moisture content.
    C. the type of tree from which it came.
    D. the temperature of the surrounding air.

_____ 3. Wood with high moisture content is sometimes referred to as: (142)
    A. old wood.
    B. green wood.
    C. pressure treated.
    D. highly flammable.

_____ 4. How does applying water to burning wood minimize damage? (142)
    A. By washing away soot
    B. By saponifying the fuel
    C. By washing away contaminants
    D. By stopping the charring process

_____ 5. Which of the following statements about particleboard, fiberboard, and paneling is MOST accurate? (142)
    A. They have a higher ignition point.
    B. They are not usually combustible.
    C. They can produce significant toxic gases.
    D. They are highly tolerant of fire conditions.

_____ 6. Which of the following types of walls is designed to limit the spread of a fire within a structure or between adjacent structures? (142)
    A. Fire wall
    B. Veneer wall
    C. Barrier wall
    D. Cantilever wall

_____ 7. What happens to stones when they are heated? (142)

    A. They melt.

    B. They may spall.

    C. They deteriorate completely.

    D. They show absolutely no effect.

_____ 8. Which of the following terms is described as a wall with a surface layer of attractive material laid over a base of common material? (142)

    A. Fire wall

    B. Veneer wall

    C. Barrier wall

    D. Cantilever wall

_____ 9. Rapid cooling may cause masonry materials to: (142)

    A. melt.

    B. crack.

    C. explode.

    D. disintegrate.

_____ 10. Which of the following effects of firefighting operations on cast iron is a primary concern to firefighters? (143)

    A. Cast iron may melt, causing molten metal to flow toward bystanders.

    B. Cast iron may splinter into tiny pieces, causing a spray of metal shards to fill the surrounding air.

    C. Masonry behind the cast iron may crack, causing the entire section of metal to fall forward.

    D. Bolts that hold cast iron to the building may fail, causing heavy sections of metal to crash to the ground.

_____ 11. What happens to steel structural members when they are heated? (143)

    A. They shrink

    B. They smolder

    C. They elongate

    D. They strengthen

_____ 12. What happens if steel is restrained from movement at the ends? (143)

    A. It shatters.

    B. It breaks the restraint system.

    C. It buckles and fails in the middle.

    D. It shrinks and causes the walls to pull inward.

____ 13. At which of the following temperatures do steel structural members begin to fail? (143)

A. 750°F (400°C)

B. 1,000°F (538°C)

C. 1,250°F (677°C)

D. 1,500°F (815°C)

____ 14. Which of the following actions can stop elongation of steel, reducing the risk of a structural collapse? (144)

A. Applying water

B. Stopping air flow

C. Cutting the steel

D. Waiting for the fire to subside

____ 15. How does reinforced concrete lose strength under fire conditions? (144)

A. By shrinking

B. By elongating

C. Through melting

D. Through spalling

____ 16. Which of the following statements about gypsum is MOST accurate? (145)

A. It breaks down quickly under fire conditions.

B. Its water content gives it fire-retardant properties.

C. Its low water content makes it highly susceptible to heat.

D. It provides no heat protection to the steel and wood structural members which it covers.

____ 17. What may happen to heated glass when it is struck by a cold fire stream? (145)

A. It may melt.

B. It may crack.

C. It may shrink.

D. It may elongate.

____ 18. Which of the following types of glass may provide some thermal protection as a separation? (145)

A. Fiberglass

B. Frosted glass

C. Tempered glass

D. Wire-reinforced glass

_____ 19. Which of the following statements about the materials used to bind fiberglass is MOST accurate? (145)

    A. They may be combustible.

    B. They have fire-retardant properties.

    C. They are moderately combustible but extremely easy to extinguish.

    D. They are unlikely to be combustible but when they do burn, they are extremely difficult to extinguish.

_____ 20. Which of the following questions should NOT be addressed during size-up? (151)

    A. Does the structure have an arched or lightweight roof?

    B. Is it a wood-frame, unreinforced masonry, or all-metal building?

    C. What is the water composition of the soil surrounding the basement?

    D. Are there HVAC units, water tanks, or other heavy objects on the roof?

_____ 21. Which of the following size-up factors is directly related to the hazards associated with building construction? (151)

    A. Dead loads

    B. Fire conditions

    C. Occupancy type

    D. Adjacent exposures

_____ 22. The presence of large amounts of combustible materials in an area or a building is known as: (152)

    A. overloading.

    B. irresponsible.

    C. heavy fire loading.

    D. danger zone material.

_____ 23. Which of the following terms is described as the final outside cover that is placed on top of a roof deck assembly? (153)

    A. Decking

    B. Roof layer

    C. Roof covering

    D. Top assembly

_____ 24. Historically, which of the following roofing materials contributes MOST to fire spread? (153)

    A. Tin

    B. Tar

    C. Slate

    D. Wood shakes

_____ 25. Proper use of which of the following is considered MOST necessary for slowing the spread of fire in large, open spaces? (153)
    A. Forced ventilation
    B. Vertical ventilation
    C. Hydraulic ventilation
    D. Horizontal ventilation

_____ 26. Which of the following building construction features will MOST quickly succumb to the effects of fire? (154)
    A. Buildings made of steel
    B. Buildings containing gypsum
    C. Buildings of truss construction
    D. Buildings made of heavyweight construction materials

_____ 27. When should information on building age and construction type ideally be obtained? (154)
    A. During size-up
    B. Upon arrival at the fire
    C. When conducting inspections
    D. When conducting the primary search

_____ 28. Which of the following terms BEST describes the area extending horizontally from the base of the wall to one and one-half times the height of the wall? (154)
    A. Hot zone
    B. Cold zone
    C. Warm zone
    D. Collapse zone

_____ 29. Which of the following is an indicator of potential building collapse? (155-156)
    A. Absence of stars
    B. Absence of tie rods
    C. Deteriorated mortar between the masonry
    D. Fires beneath floors that support light weight loads

_____ 30. Which of the following is NOT an indicator of pending building collapse? (155-156)
    A. Walls that appear to be leaning
    B. Smoke coming from windows and doors
    C. Structural members pulling away from walls
    D. Loose bricks, blocks, or stones falling from buildings

_____ 31. Which of the following techniques can result in structural supports being cut that could weaken the structure? (156)

A. Improper vertical ventilation

B. Improper horizontal ventilation

C. Improper positive-pressure ventilation

D. Improper negative-pressure ventilation

_____ 32. Which of the following is the FIRST step that should be taken if building collapse is imminent? (156)

A. Establish a collapse zone.

B. Inform Command of the situation.

C. Cautiously place master stream devices.

D. Immediately withdraw master stream devices.

_____ 33. Which of the following is a step that should be taken if building collapse is suspected? (156)

A. Clear the collapse zone.

B. Inform the media of the situation.

C. Place manned master stream devices.

D. Immediately withdraw master stream devices.

_____ 34. Who should be allowed to operate continuously in the collapse zone? (156)

A. Command

B. No personnel

C. The primary search team

D. A rapid intervention crew

_____ 35. What happens to the risk of fire when construction, renovation, or demolition is being performed in a structure? (158)

A. It is minimal.

B. It is nonexistent.

C. It increases sharply.

D. It decreases sharply.

_____ 36. Which of the following factors causes new buildings under construction to be subject to rapid fire spread? (158)

A. Closed floors

B. Presence of a rain roof

C. Lack of doors that would normally slow fire spread

D. Fire alarm systems that may have been taken out of service

_____ 37. Which of the following terms is described as a second roof constructed over an older leaky roof? (158)
  A. Rain roof
  B. Secondary roof
  C. Water protection system
  D. Replacement roof system

_____ 38. If everyone has escaped the building and the structure itself is the only thing at risk, the most likely method of fighting the fire is: (159)
  A. offensive attack.
  B. defensive attack.
  C. from the inside.
  D. from the burned side.

_____ 39. What happens when contractors add a mansard fascia to a building? (158-159)
  A. A fire hazard is avoided.
  B. A concealed space is created.
  C. The risk of arson is increased.
  D. The potential for undetected fire spread is decreased.

_____ 40. What must be done before fire officers order firefighters to fight a fire inside a building under construction? (159)
  A. Primary search
  B. Secondary search
  C. Preincident survey
  D. Risk/benefit analysis

Firefighter II

Chapter 5

Firefighter Personal Protective Equipment

_____ 1. Which of the following protects the trunk and limbs against cuts, abrasions, and burn injuries; protects the body from heat and cold; and provides limited protection from corrosive liquids? (168)

   A. Gloves

   B. Protective hood

   C. Safety shoes or boots

   D. Protective coat and trousers

_____ 2. Which of the following provides an audible means by which a lost, trapped, or incapacitated firefighter can be located? (168)

   A. Personal GPS system

   B. Individual location beacon (ILB)

   C. Personal alert safety system (PASS)

   D. Personal signal and sound system (PSSS)

_____ 3. Which of the following protects the face and lungs from heat, smoke and other toxic products of combustion, and airborne contaminants? (168)

   A. Helmet

   B. Protective hood

   C. Eye protection

   D. Self-contained breathing apparatus (SCBA)

_____ 4. Which of the following statements about equipment worn by the firefighter is MOST accurate? (169)

   A. It should be less than 10 years old.

   B. It should be less than 5 years old.

   C. It should meet current applicable standards.

   D. It only needs to meet standards applicable at time of purchase.

_____ 5. Which of the following is NOT a benefit of structural fire fighting helmets? (169)

   A. Protects the head from impact

   B. Provides hearing protection

   C. Provides protection from heat and cold

   D. Provides unit and rank identification when colored

_____ 6. Structural fire fighting helmets must have: (169)

  A. holes for ventilation.

  B. ear flaps or neck covers.

  C. built-in cooling systems.

  D. adjustable inset padding for sizing.

_____ 7. Which of the following is an example of a situation where eye protection greater than that provided by a helmet faceshield is needed, but respiratory protection is not needed? (170)

  A. Small structural fires

  B. Salvage and overhaul operations

  C. Chemical or hazardous materials incidents

  D. Medical calls where exposure to bodily fluids is possible

_____ 8. The most common use of hearing protection is for firefighters who: (171)

  A. are inspecting industrial occupancies.

  B. are sleeping or resting in the fire station.

  C. are engaged in structural fire fighting activities.

  D. ride apparatus that exceed maximum noise exposure levels.

_____ 9. Which of the following personnel should always wear hearing protection? (172)

  A. Those operating power tools

  B. Those operating hand tools

  C. Those involved in structural fire fighting

  D. Those operating at mass casualty incidents

_____ 10. Which of the following is designed to protect your ears, neck, and face from exposure to heat, hot embers, and debris? (172)

  A. Helmets

  B. Protective hoods

  C. Hearing protection devices

  D. Safety goggles

_____ 11. Which of the following lists the components required by NFPA® 1971 for structural fire fighting protective coats? (173)

  A. Outer shell and inner lining

  B. Outer shell, outer lining, inner lining

  C. Outer shell, middle shell, thermal barrier

  D. Outer shell, moisture barrier, thermal barrier

_____ 12. Which of the following statements about the use and limitations of PPE is MOST accurate? (173)
    A. Damaged PPE will put you at greater risk.
    B. PPE increases your ability to feel ambient heat.
    C. Wearing PPE decreases your risk of heat stress.
    D. Structural PPE provides chemical and biological protection.

_____ 13. Which of the following is a built-in harness and hand loop at the back of the neck of a turnout coat that permits a rescuer to grab and drag a downed firefighter? (174)
    A. Drag Rescue Device (DRD)
    B. Loop Rescue Strap (LRS)
    C. Emergency Drag System (EDS)
    D. Coat Loop Rescue Device (CLRD)

_____ 14. Protective trousers should be cleaned: (176)
    A. according to manufacturer's specifications.
    B. in the same manner as work station clothing.
    C. in the same manner as hand-washable clothing.
    D. by whatever means removes the dirt and debris.

_____ 15. Which of the following statements about hand protection is MOST accurate? (176)
    A. Gloves do not provide protection against steam or liquid absorption.
    B. Gloves can always provide protection without any reduction in dexterity.
    C. When wearing gloves, it is not important for the wearer to be able to grasp or manipulate small objects.
    D. Gloves must allow enough dexterity and tactile feel for the firefighter to perform the job effectively.

_____ 16. Firefighters should have foot protection that includes protective boots for fire fighting and similar emergencies and: (176)
    A. hip-length waders for water.
    B. hiking boots for outdoor tasks.
    C. one pair of shoes of their choice for station wear.
    D. safety shoes for station wear and other fire department tasks.

_____ 17. Which of the following would be the MOST appropriate material for wildland fire fighting clothing? (177)
    A. Nylon
    B. Polyester
    C. Treated cotton
    D. Any fabric that is comfortable

_____ 18. Boots used in wildland fire fighting should be at least _____ high to protect the lower leg from burns, snakebites, and cuts and abrasions. (178)
- A. 2 to 4 inches (50 mm to 100 mm)
- B. 4 to 6 inches (100 mm to 150 mm)
- C. 6 to 8 inches (150 mm to 200 mm)
- D. 8 to 10 inches (200 mm to 250 mm)

_____ 19. Which of the following statements about station/work uniforms is MOST accurate? (178)
- A. They do not need to be fire resistant.
- B. They can be worn for nuisance fire fighting calls.
- C. They are not required to meet any specific standards.
- D. They are not designed to be worn for fire fighting operations.

_____ 20. Contamination of protective garments by hydrocarbons: (179)
- A. increases their fire resistiveness.
- B. decreases their fire resistiveness.
- C. has no effect on their fire resistiveness.
- D. can either increase or decrease their fire resistiveness.

_____ 21. What should be done with polycarbonate fire fighting helmets that have come into contact with hydraulic oil? (179)
- A. They should be removed from service.
- B. They should be washed with soap and warm water.
- C. They should be used only for training purposes.
- D. The oil should be blotted with a towel and then rubbed off.

_____ 22. According to NFPA® 1581, _Standard on Fire Department Infection Control Program_, personal protective clothing should be cleaned and dried at least every _____ in accordance with the manufacturer's recommendations. (180)
- A. 2 months
- B. 6 months
- C. 12 months
- D. 18 months

_____ 23. After PPE has been washed, it should be hung to dry in an area with: (180)
- A. adequate ventilation but not in direct sunlight.
- B. direct sunlight and substantial ventilation.
- C. no noticeable ventilation and a source of natural light.
- D. adequate ventilation and room to hang garments in direct sunlight.

_____ 24. Which of the following ways that toxic products can enter the body is of the most concern to firefighters? (180)

A. Ingestion

B. Inhalation

C. Absorption

D. Permeation

_____ 25. Which of the following is NOT one of the common respiratory hazards associated with fires and other emergencies? (180)

A. Smoke

B. Elevated oxygen

C. Elevated temperatures

D. Toxic atmospheres

_____ 26. Both OSHA and NFPA® define an oxygen-deficient atmosphere as one containing less than _____ percent oxygen. (181)

A. 12

B. 15.5

C. 17.5

D. 19.5

_____ 27. Which of the following can result from inhaling heated gases? (181)

A. Pulmonary edema

B. Heat stroke

C. Heat exhaustion

D. Increased blood pressure

_____ 28. Which of the following results in more fire deaths than any other toxic product of combustion? (183)

A. Carbon dioxide

B. Carbon monoxide

C. Hydrogen chloride

D. Hydrogen cyanide

_____ 29. Which of the following is NOT a primary sign or symptom of carbon monoxide exposure? (184)

A. Headaches

B. Dizziness

C. Cherry-red skin

D. Excessive thirst

_____ 30. Which of the following is used in manufacturing plastics, foam rubber, and synthetic textiles and is commonly found at water and sewage treatment plants? (185)
   A. Chlorine
   B. Ammonia
   C. Sulfur dioxide
   D. Carbon dioxide

_____ 31. Which of the following is the MOST likely warning sign that the atmosphere may be toxic at a vehicle accident involving a commercial truck? (187)
   A. Size of the truck
   B. Placard on the truck
   C. Number of casualties
   D. Presence or absence of bystanders

_____ 32. Which of the following is a physical factor that can affect firefighters' ability to use respiratory protection effectively? (187)
   A. Facial features
   B. Self-confidence
   C. Emotional stability
   D. Neurological functioning

_____ 33. Which of the following factors related to the ability to use respiratory protection effectively refers to the ability to maintain control in claustrophobic and stressful environments? (188)
   A. Self-confidence
   B. Emotional stability
   C. Respiratory functioning
   D. Cardiovascular conditioning

_____ 34. Which of the following is an equipment limitation of respiratory protection? (188)
   A. Agility
   B. Increased weight
   C. Decreased weight
   D. Adequate training in equipment use

_____ 35. Those in poor physical condition expend their air supply: (188)
   A. faster than others performing the same tasks.
   B. slower than others performing the same tasks.
   C. at the same rate as those performing the same tasks.
   D. either faster or slower than those performing the same tasks.

_____ 36. Who makes the decision to stay or leave the hazard zone if no catastrophic event has occurred? (189)
  A. Supervisor
  B. Individual firefighter
  C. Senior firefighter
  D. Training officer

_____ 37. Which of the following terms refers to that time at which the remaining operation time of the SCBA is equal to the time necessary to return safely to a nonhazardous atmosphere? (189)
  A. Point of no return
  B. Low-alarm base time
  C. Maximum time of exit
  D. Minimum time of exit

_____ 38. At the beginning of your shift, you should make sure the SCBA cylinder is at least: (190)
  A. 50 percent full.
  B. 60 percent full.
  C. 75 percent full.
  D. 90 percent full.

_____ 39. Which of the following types of respiratory protection uses compressed air? (190)
  A. Open-circuit SCBA
  B. Closed-circuit SCBA
  C. Air-purifying respirators
  D. Closed-circuit airline equipment

_____ 40. Which of the following types of respiratory protection uses compressed oxygen? (190)
  A. Open-circuit SCBA
  B. Closed-circuit SCBA
  C. Air-purifying respirators
  D. Closed-circuit airline equipment

_____ 41. Which of the following types of respiratory protection is MOST likely to be used in shipboard operations, extended hazardous materials incidents, and some rescue operations? (190)
  A. Open-circuit SCBA
  B. Closed-circuit SCBA
  C. Air-purifying respirators
  D. Closed-circuit airline equipment

_____ 42. Which of the following basic SCBA component assemblies includes a high-pressure hose with low-pressure alarm, by-pass valve, and a pressure-reducing device? (190)
   A.   Harness assembly
   B.   Regulator assembly
   C.   Facepiece assembly
   D.   Air cylinder assembly

_____ 43. Which of the following basic SCBA component assemblies includes a rigid frame with straps that hold the air cylinder on the firefighter's back? (190)
   A.   Harness assembly
   B.   Regulator assembly
   C.   Facepiece assembly
   D.   Air cylinder assembly

_____ 44. Which of the following basic SCBA component assemblies constitutes the main weight of the breathing apparatus? (191)
   A.   Harness assembly
   B.   Regulator assembly
   C.   Facepiece assembly
   D.   Air cylinder assembly

_____ 45. On an SCBA, the regulator reduces the pressure of the cylinder air to _____ atmospheric pressure and controls the flow of air to meet the respiratory requirements of the wearer. (192)
   A.   slightly above
   B.   slightly below
   C.   the same as
   D.   within 10 percent above or below

_____ 46. The remote pressure gauge on the regulator assembly should read within _____ of the cylinder gauge if increments are in psi (kPa). (193)
   A.   25 psi (175 kPa)
   B.   50 psi (350 kPa)
   C.   75 psi (525 kPa)
   D.   100 psi (700 kPa)

_____ 47. Which of the following allows a cylinder that is low on air to be transfilled from another cylinder regardless of the manufacturer? (194)
   A.   Standard SCBA air connection
   B.   Rapid intervention global SCBA plug-in
   C.   Universal transfill emergency connection
   D.   Rapid intervention crew universal air connection

_____ 48. Which of the following is NOT a part of the facepiece assembly? (194)

   A. Facepiece lens

   B. Mainline valve

   C. Exhalation valve

   D. Low-pressure hose

_____ 49. Which of the following components displays the current cylinder pressure on the inside of the facepiece lens or mask-mounted regulator and allows the wearer to monitor the air supply without having to read an external gauge? (195)

   A. Heads-up display

   B. Low-pressure alarm

   C. Remote pressure gauge

   D. External regulator gauge

_____ 50. Which of the following methods of controlling internal fogging of the facepiece lens deflects exhalations away from the lens? (197)

   A. Nosecup

   B. Antifogging chemical

   C. Full facepiece blower

   D. Forced exhalation valve

_____ 51. Which of the following types of respiratory protection allows firefighters to travel up to 300 feet (100 m) from the air supply source, allowing them to work for hours if necessary without the encumbrance of a backpack? (197)

   A. Open-circuit SCBA

   B. Closed-circuit SCBA

   C. Air-purifying respirators

   D. Open-circuit airline equipment

_____ 52. Which of the following is NOT a standard method of storing self-contained breathing apparatus? (198)

   A. Seat mounts

   B. Hood mounts

   C. Carrying cases

   D. Compartment mounts

_____ 53. The use of personal alert safety system (PASS) devices by all firefighters and rescuers wearing SCBA is mandatory under: (198)

   A. NFPA® 1002.

   B. NFPA® 1021.

   C. NFPA® 1041.

   D. NFPA® 1500.

_____ 54. If a firefighter wearing a PASS device should remain motionless for approximately _____, the device will emit a loud, pulsating shriek. (199)

A. 10 seconds

B. 30 seconds

C. 3 minutes

D. 5 minutes

_____ 55. If the remote gauge and the cylinder gauge are not marked in increments of 100 psi (700 kPa) they should read: (200)

A. the same.

B. within 5% of each other.

C. within 10% of each other.

D. within 20% of each other.

_____ 56. Which of the following methods of donning SCBA allows firefighters to don SCBA while en route to an incident? (201)

A. Seat mount

B. Side mount

C. Rear mount

D. Compartment mount

_____ 57. Which of the following methods of donning SCBA eliminates some steps but also exposes the units to weather and physical damage? (202)

A. Seat mount

B. Side mount

C. Backup mount

D. Compartment mount

_____ 58. Interchanging facepieces, or any other part of the SCBA, from one manufacturer's equipment to another: (203)

A. makes any warranty and certification void.

B. can be done if the models are essentially the same.

C. can save money by prolonging equipment life.

D. is encouraged by manufacturers of self-contained breathing apparatus.

_____ 59. Which of the following NFPA® standards requires that each firefighter be fitted with a facepiece that conforms properly to the shape and size of his or her face? (203)

A. NFPA® 1002

B. NFPA® 1021

C. NFPA® 1041

D. NFPA® 1500

60. How can positive pressure be checked on the SCBA facepiece? (204)
   A. By removing the facepiece entirely
   B. By gently breaking the facepiece seal
   C. By holding your breath for 30 seconds
   D. By inhaling several breaths very quickly

61. Which of the following is an action that applies to all SCBA when doffing? (204)
   A. Open the cylinder valve.
   B. Attach the regulator to the facepiece.
   C. Connect the low-pressure hose to the regulator.
   D. Make sure you are out of the contaminated area.

62. After checking the bypass valve when inspecting SCBA, you should make sure it is: (205)
   A. fully open.
   B. fully closed.
   C. partially open.
   D. in the middle position.

63. Breathing apparatus should be cleaned and sanitized: (205)
   A. immediately after each use.
   B. after being used several times.
   C. within 48 hours of being used.
   D. within 72 hours of being used.

64. Which of the following actions can damage SCBA and should be avoided? (206)
   A. Allowing the facepiece to air dry
   B. Using a lint-free cloth on the facepiece
   C. Using paper towels to dry the facepiece lens
   D. Using a mild commercial disinfectant on the facepiece

65. Annual maintenance, testing and repairs requiring the expertise of factory-certified technicians should be done: (206)
   A. in accordance with manufacturer's recommendations.
   B. by firefighters who have watched factory technicians.
   C. only if the SCBA is no longer functioning in any manner.
   D. when the department cannot afford to replace the SCBA units.

_____ 66. Which of the following is a safety precaution for refilling SCBA cylinders? (206)

A. Ensure that the cylinder is two-thirds full.

B. Ensure that the cylinder is three-quarters full.

C. Prevent the cylinder from overheating by filling quickly.

D. Prevent the cylinder from overheating by filling slowly.

_____ 67. All firefighters who are certified to wear SCBA must be fit tested _____ or when new facepieces are issued to determine proper fit of the facepiece. (208)

A. every 6 months

B. annually

C. every 2 years

D. every 3 years

_____ 68. While in any Immediately Dangerous to Life or Health (IDLH) atmosphere, firefighters must work: (208)

A. in teams of two or more.

B. in teams of four or more.

C. on the same floor.

D. within radio range of each other.

_____ 69. Which of the following is the MOST important when dealing with emergencies created by malfunctioning breathing apparatus? (208)

A. Take care of the situation yourself

B. Continue to engage in fire fighting operations

C. Inhale the remaining air as deeply and as quickly as possible.

D. Immediate withdrawal from the hazardous atmosphere

_____ 70. When dealing with an emergency created by malfunctioning breathing, apparatus, if you are lost or disoriented and feel exhausted or you might lose consciousness you should: (210)

A. lie flat on the floor close to a wall.

B. lie flat on the floor in the middle of a room.

C. continue to try and find a way out yourself.

D. get onto a higher object such as a chair or bed and lie down.

_____ 71. When working in areas of limited visibility, which of the following methods of moving about allows firefighters to remain close to the floor and feel for victims? (211)

A. Crawling

B. Slithering on the stomach

C. Standing with back slightly bent over

D. Alternating standing and crouching

72. Which of the following would NOT be an appropriate tag line for use in an Immediately Dangerous to Life or Health (IDLH) atmosphere? (211)
    A. Rope
    B. Hoseline
    C. Electrical cord
    D. Hydraulic hoses from rescue tools

73. Which of the following methods of moving about in an area of limited visibility should be used only if firefighters can see the floor? (211)
    A. Crawling
    B. Crouching
    C. Standing with back slightly bent over
    D. Alternating standing and crouching

74. Which of the following is NOT a general guideline for exiting areas with restricted openings under emergency conditions while wearing SCBA? (211)
    A. Loosen straps as necessary to reduce your profile.
    B. Maintain contact with belt-mounted regulators at all times.
    C. Push the SCBA in front of you, maintaining control of the SCBA at all times.
    D. Pull the SCBA in back of you, maintaining control of the SCBA at all times.

75. Which of the following statements about changing SCBA cylinders is MOST accurate? (212)
    A. Changing cylinders is always a two-person job.
    B. Changing cylinders is not the job of a firefighter.
    C. All cylinders should be kept in the same area.
    D. Empty cylinders should be segregated from cylinders that are serviced and ready for use.

Chapter 6

Portable Fire Extinguishers

_____ 1. Which of the following types of portable fire extinguishers is designed to extinguish Class A fires only? (235)
   A. Halon 1301
   B. Clean agent
   C. Dry chemical
   D. Stored-pressure water

_____ 2. Which of the following types of portable fire extinguishers is designed to extinguish Class A and B fires only? (235)
   A. Dry powder
   B. Wet chemical
   C. Pump-tank water
   D. Aqueous film forming foam

_____ 3. Which of the following types of portable fire extinguishers is designed to extinguish Class A, B, and C fires? (235)
   A. Dry chemical
   B. Carbon dioxide
   C. Stored-pressure water
   D. Aqueous film forming foam

_____ 4. Which of the following types of portable fire extinguishers is designed to extinguish Class D fires only? (235)
   A. Halon 1211
   B. Dry powder
   C. Clean agent
   D. Wet chemical

_____ 5. Which of the following types of portable fire extinguishers is designed to extinguish Class K fires only? (235)
   A. Dry chemical
   B. Wet chemical
   C. Pump-tank water
   D. Multipurpose dry chemical

_____ 6. Which of the following types of fire is a Halon 1211 portable fire extinguisher designed to extinguish? (235)

    A. Class A

    B. Class D

    C. Class B and C

    D. Class A and K

_____ 7. Which of the following types of fire is a pump-tank water portable fire extinguisher designed to extinguish? (235)

    A. Class A

    B. Class B

    C. Class D

    D. Class K

_____ 8. Which of the following types of fire is a clean agent portable fire extinguisher designed to extinguish? (235)

    A. Class B only

    B. Class K only

    C. Class A, B, and C

    D. Class B, C, and D

_____ 9. Which of the following types of fire is a carbon dioxide portable fire extinguisher designed to extinguish? (235)

    A. Class A and D

    B. Class A and K

    C. Class B and C

    D. Class B and D

_____ 10. Which of the following types of fire is a multipurpose dry chemical portable fire extinguisher designed to extinguish? (235)

    A. Class D only

    B. Class K only

    C. Class A and D

    D. Class A, B, and C

_____ 11. What will happen to a fire in magnesium if water is applied? (235)

    A. The fire will be saponified.

    B. The fire will be extinguished.

    C. The fire will flare up and intensify.

    D. The fire will diminish considerably.

_____ 12. NFPA®1901, *Standard for Automotive Fire Apparatus*, requires that pumping apparatus have how many approved portable fire extinguishers with mounting brackets? (235)

    A. One

    B. Two

    C. Three

    D. Four

_____ 13. Fire extinguisher ratings represent the type of fire and: (236)

    A. fire intensity.

    B. difficulty of use.

    C. extinguisher weight.

    D. performance capability.

_____ 14. Which of the following methods is NOT a mechanism by which portable fire extinguishers expel their contents? (236)

    A. Manual pump

    B. Electric pump

    C. Stored pressure

    D. Pressure cartridge

_____ 15. Which type of fire involves ordinary combustibles such as textiles, paper, plastics, rubber, and wood? (236-237)

    A. Class A

    B. Class B

    C. Class C

    D. Class D

_____ 16. Which of the following is an example of a Class K fire? (236-237)

    A. A fire involving wood

    B. A fire involving electrical energy

    C. A fire involving combustible metals

    D. A fire involving combustible cooking oils

_____ 17. Which type of fire involves electrical energy? (236-237)

    A. Class A

    B. Class B

    C. Class C

    D. Class D

_____ 18. Which of the following is an example of a Class D fire? (236-237)
   A. A fire involving flammable gases
   B. A fire involving electrical energy
   C. A fire involving combustible metals
   D. A fire involving combustible cooking oils

_____ 19. Which type of fire involves flammable and combustible liquids, gases, and greases? (236-237)
   A. Class B
   B. Class C
   C. Class D
   D. Class K

_____ 20. How can Class D fires be identified? (237)
   A. By dark, thick smoke from the combustion process
   B. By bright white emissions from the combustion process
   C. By various colors of emissions from the combustion process
   D. By glowing red and orange emissions from the combustion process

_____ 21. In stored-pressure water extinguishers, water is stored in a tank with compressed air or: (237)
   A. plasma.
   B. oxygen.
   C. nitrogen.
   D. carbon dioxide.

_____ 22. What can be added to stored-pressure water extinguishers to increase their effectiveness? (237)
   A. Dry chemicals
   B. Class A foam
   C. Class C foam
   D. Potassium chloride

_____ 23. What type of water is used in water-mist fire extinguishers? (239)
   A. Heated water
   B. Ordinary tap water
   C. Chilled ionized water
   D. Deionized distilled water

24. What kind of agent is used by wet chemical stored-pressure extinguishers to cool and suppress fires in unsaturated cooking oils? (239)
    A. Alkaline agent
    B. Low-pH agent
    C. Nitrogen-based agent
    D. Monoammonium-based agent

25. On which type of fire are aqueous film forming foam (AFFF) extinguishers suitable for use? (241)
    A. Class B fires
    B. Class C fires
    C. Fuel flowing down from an elevated point
    D. Fuel under pressure spraying from a leaking flange

26. Which of the following statements about clean agent extinguishers is MOST accurate? (241)
    A. They are conductive.
    B. They are pressurized with hydrogen gas.
    C. They effectively cool and smother fires in Class A and B fuels.
    D. They are not approved by the U.S. Environmental Protection Agency.

27. Which of the following statements about carbon dioxide extinguishers is LEAST accurate? (241)
    A. They have a limited reach.
    B. They require freeze protection.
    C. Their discharge is in the form of a gas.
    D. They are most effective in extinguishing Class B and C fires.

28. Which of the following types of fires requires a dry powder agent? (243)
    A. Class A
    B. Class D
    C. Class A, B, and C
    D. Class B, C, and D

29. Which of the following is a basic design for handheld dry chemical extinguishers? (244)
    A. Stored pressure
    B. Nonpressurized
    C. Nozzle-operated
    D. Single-acting pump

_____ 30. Which of the following agents is used in handheld dry chemical extinguishers? (244)
  A. Oxygen
  B. Hydrogen
  C. Chlorine gas
  D. Carbon dioxide

_____ 31. When a dry chemical wheeled unit is in position at a fire, the hose should be: (244)
  A. disconnected.
  B. coiled next to the unit.
  C. stretched out completely.
  D. coiled only until the nozzle is opened.

_____ 32. What can happen when the crust over burning metal is broken? (245-246)
  A. The fire may flare up.
  B. Hot spots will be eliminated.
  C. The fire will be extinguished.
  D. The exposure of uninvolved material will be prevented.

_____ 33. Which of the following is the act of excluding oxygen from a fuel? (246)
  A. Cooling
  B. Starving
  C. Smothering
  D. Saponifying

_____ 34. Upon which of the following factors is the Class A water extinguisher rating based? (247)
  A. Toxicity of the agent
  B. Electrical conductivity
  C. The amount of extinguishing agent and the duration and range of the discharge used in extinguishing test fires
  D. The approximate square foot (square meter) area of a flammable liquid fire that a nonexpert operator can extinguish

_____ 35. Upon which of the following factors is the Class B extinguisher rating based? (247)
  A. Toxicity of the agent
  B. Electrical conductivity
  C. The amount of extinguishing agent and the duration and range of the discharge used in extinguishing test fires
  D. The approximate square foot (square meter) area of a flammable liquid fire that a nonexpert operator can extinguish

_____ 36. Which of the following statements about Class D fire extinguisher ratings is MOST accurate? (248)

A. A numerical rating is given in application instructions.

B. The reactions between the metal and the agent are considered during test fires.

C. Class D agents can be given a multipurpose rating for use on other classes of fire.

D. Application instructions should not be included on the faceplate of the extinguisher.

_____ 37. Which of the following terms is described as converting fatty acids or fats to a soap or foam? (248)

A. Cooling

B. Smothering

C. Saponifying

D. Chain breaking

_____ 38. How are extinguishers suitable for more than one class of fire identified? (248)

A. By using a blended color on the extinguisher itself

B. By detailed descriptions indicating the fires they can be used on

C. By new letters that indicate the combined use of the extinguisher

D. By combinations of the letters A, B, and/or C or the symbols for each class

_____ 39. Which of the following is NOT an item to check immediately before using a portable fire extinguisher? (250)

A. Weight

B. Capacity

C. Hose/nozzle

D. Pressure gauge

_____ 40. The "P" in the PASS method of application stands for: (251)

A. "Pull the pin."

B. "Pump the handle."

C. "Penetrate the fuel."

D. "Position the nozzle."

_____ 41. The "A" in the PASS method of application stands for: (251)

A. "Aim the nozzle."

B. "Arrange the hose."

C. "Activate the system."

D. "Aspirate the contents."

_____ 42. The first "S" in the PASS method of application stands for: (251)

A. "Smother the fire."

B. "Start extinguishing."

C. "Squeeze the handles together."

D. "Sweep the nozzle back and forth."

_____ 43. The second "S" in the PASS method of application stands for: (251)

A. "Smother the fire."

B. "Start extinguishing."

C. "Squeeze the handles together."

D. "Sweep the nozzle back and forth."

_____ 44. How often does NFPA® 10 require that portable fire extinguishers be inspected? (252)

A. Biannually

B. Once yearly

C. Twice yearly

D. Once monthly

_____ 45. Who is responsible for servicing portable fire extinguishers? (252)

A. The manufacturer

B. The fire department

C. The property owner

D. The code enforcement officer

_____ 46. Which of the following is NOT a factor that determines the value of a fire extinguisher? (252)

A. Its cost

B. Its accessibility

C. Its serviceability

D. Its simplicity of operation

_____ 47. Which of the following actions should be taken if an extinguisher shows only slight damage but it is uncertain whether the unit is safe to use? (253)

A. It should be discarded immediately.

B. It should be closely monitored while in use.

C. It should be hydrostatically tested by the manufacturer.

D. The safety officer should be consulted for determination of the unit's effectiveness.

_____ 48. The Montreal Protocol on Substances that Deplete the Ozone Layer required: (254)
  A. use of halogens in all Class C fire extinguishers.
  B. use of halogens in all Class K fire extinguishers.
  C. complete termination of the production and consumption of halogens by the year 2000.
  D. complete termination of the production and consumption of halogens by the year 2015.

_____ 49. Which of the following statements related to halogen extinguishers is MOST accurate? (254)
  A. Halogenated vapor conducts electricity on energized equipment.
  B. Halogenated vapor is ineffective on energized electrical equipment.
  C. Halogenated agents extinguish fire by interrupting the chain reaction of the combustion process.
  D. Halogenated agents are effective on fires in self-oxidizing fuels such as organic peroxides and metal hydrides.

_____ 50. Halon 1211 has been replaced by: (254)
  A. FE-36™ hexafluoropropane.
  B. FM-200™ heptafluropropane.
  C. FE-241™ chlorotetrafluoroethane.
  D. FY-290™ chlorohexafluoroethylene.

_____ 1. The two classifications of fire service rope are utility rope and: (264)
   A. station rope.
   B. service rope.
   C. life-safety rope.
   D. weight-bearing rope.

_____ 2. Which of the following is a criteria to consider before a life-safety rope is reused in life-safety situations? (264)
   A. Rope is less than one year old.
   B. Rope is less than two years old.
   C. Rope has not been impact loaded.
   D. Rope has not been used in any life-safety situation.

_____ 3. If a life-safety rope fails to pass inspection or has been impact loaded it should be: (265)
   A. used as a back-up life-safety rope.
   B. used for life-safety applications only in training.
   C. repaired and inspected again for life-safety use.
   D. altered in such a manner that it cannot be mistaken for life-safety rope.

_____ 4. Which of the following is NOT an acceptable use for utility rope? (265)
   A. Hoisting equipment
   B. Cordoning off an area
   C. Securing unstable objects
   D. Training in life-safety applications

_____ 5. Which of the following is a characteristic of synthetic rope? (265)
   A. Limited strength
   B. Difficult to maintain
   C. Prone to mildew and rotting
   D. Excellent resistance to mildew and rotting

_____ 6. Which of the following is made of hemp or cotton? (265)
   A. Dynamic rope
   B. Synthetic rope
   C. Kernmantle rope
   D. Natural fiber rope

_____ 7. Which of the following types of rope is used when long falls are a possibility and is designed to stretch without breaking? (267)
   A. Laid rope
   B. Static rope
   C. Dynamic rope
   D. Braid-on-braid rope

_____ 8. Which of the following types of rope is used for most rope-rescue incidents and is designed for low stretch without breaking? (267)
   A. Laid rope
   B. Static rope
   C. Dynamic rope
   D. Braid-on-braid rope

_____ 9. Which of the following categories of life-safety rope is intended to support the weight of one person and has a maximum safe working load limit of 300 pounds (136 kg)? (267)
   A. Throwline
   B. Escape rope
   C. Light-use rope
   D. General-use rope

_____ 10. Which of the following categories of life-safety rope is intended to support the weight of two persons and has a maximum safe working load limit of 600 pounds (272 kg)? (267)
   A. Throwline
   B. Escape rope
   C. Light-use rope
   D. General-use rope

_____ 11. Which of the following categories of life-safety rope is used to tether rescuers during water rescues or to throw to a victim in the water? (267)
   A. Throwline
   B. Escape rope
   C. Light-use rope
   D. General-use rope

_____ 12. Which of the following categories of rope is intended to be used one time only and then destroyed? (267)
- A. Throwline
- B. Escape rope
- C. Light-use rope
- D. General-use rope

_____ 13. Which of the following types of rope is composed of a braided covering or sheath over a core of the main load-bearing strands and is used as life-safety rope? (267-268)
- A. Laid rope
- B. Braided rope
- C. Kernmantle rope
- D. Natural fiber rope

_____ 14. Which of the following types of rope is most commonly used as a sport rope for recreational rock or ice climbing? (268)
- A. Laid rope
- B. Braid-on-braid rope
- C. Low-stretch kernmantle rope
- D. High-stretch kernmantle rope

_____ 15. Which of the following types of rope is most commonly used as rescue rope where stretch is an undesirable characteristic? (268)
- A. Laid rope
- B. Braid-on-braid rope
- C. Low-stretch kernmantle rope
- D. High-stretch kernmantle rope

_____ 16. Which of the following types of rope is constructed by twisting yarns together to form strands and is almost exclusively used as utility rope? (268)
- A. Laid rope
- B. Braided rope
- C. Braid-on-braid rope
- D. Kernmantle rope

_____ 17. Which of the following types of rope is constructed by uniformly intertwining strands of rope together and is most commonly used as utility rope? (268)
- A. Laid rope
- B. Braided rope
- C. Braid-on-braid rope
- D. Kernmantle rope

_____ 18. Which of the following types of rope is a jacketed rope constructed with both a braided core and a braided sheath and is most often used in utility applications? (268-269)

A. Laid rope

B. Braided rope

C. Braid-on-braid rope

D. Kernmantle rope

_____ 19. All types of rope should be inspected: (269)

A. weekly.

B. monthly.

C. after each use.

D. after several consecutive uses.

_____ 20. Which of the following statements about inspecting rope is MOST accurate? (269)

A. Document inspections if time allows.

B. Document all inspections in the rope log.

C. Document only annual inspections in the rope log.

D. Document inspections only if damage is found.

_____ 21. How often should unused ropes be inspected? (269)

A. At least monthly

B. At least annually

C. At least once every three years

D. Inspection of unused ropes in not necessary

_____ 22. What should you do if the rope inspection finds imbedded shards of glass, metal shavings, wood splinters, or other foreign objects that could cause damage? (269)

A. Use it for utility rope only

B. Take the rope out of service

C. Flag it to check during next inspection

D. Attach a note that the rope should be used with caution

_____ 23. During inspections, which of the following types of rope should be checked for damage to the core and sheath? (269)

A. Laid rope

B. Braided rope

C. Kernmantle rope

D. Laid and braided rope

24. During inspections, which of the following types of rope should be untwisted and checked internally for flaws? (270)
    A. Laid rope
    B. Braided rope
    C. Kernmantle rope
    D. Laid and braided rope

25. During inspections, which of the following types of rope should be inspected for the sheath sliding on the core? (270)
    A. Laid rope
    B. Braided rope
    C. Braid-on-braid rope
    D. Laid and braided rope

26. When a piece of rescue rope is purchased, it must be: (270)
    A. permanently identified.
    B. assigned to one specific person.
    C. sent to the manufacturer for testing.
    D. sent to an independent lab for testing.

27. Which of the following is LEAST likely to damage synthetic fiber ropes during cleaning? (271)
    A. Bleach and hot water
    B. Bleach and cool water
    C. Mild soap and cool water
    D. Strong cleaners and mild water

28. Which of the following statements about cleaning natural fiber rope is MOST accurate? (271)
    A. Water weakens and damages the fiber over time.
    B. Water and mild soap can be used to clean natural fiber rope.
    C. Water should be used by itself to clean natural fiber rope.
    D. Over time, water will eventually strengthen natural fiber rope.

29. Which of the following methods provides a more thorough cleaning of synthetic rope? (271)
    A. Washing by hand
    B. Using a special rope-washing device
    C. Letting it sit overnight in a wash basin
    D. Placing it in a front-loading washing machine

_____ 30. Which of the following is NOT an appropriate way to dry rope? (272)

A. Suspended in a hose tower

B. Loosely coiled in a hose dryer

C. Spread out on a hose rack in direct sunlight

D. Spread out an a hose rack out of direct sunlight

_____ 31. Where should rescue rope be stored? (272)

A. Wherever there is adequate room in the fire station

B. In spaces or compartments that provide moisture and ventilation

C. In spaces or compartments that are clean and dry without ventilation

D. In spaces or compartments that are clean and dry and have adequate ventilation

_____ 32. Which of the following is the BEST method for storing kernmantle rope and other life-safety rope? (272)

A. Placing it in a storage bag

B. Hanging it on a storage hook

C. Leaving it laid out without kinks or bends

D. Leaving it laid out in a large circular pattern

_____ 33. Which of the following statements about webbing is MOST accurate? (273)

A. The same precautions and maintenance procedures used for synthetic rope apply to webbing.

B. The same precautions and maintenance procedures used for natural rope apply to webbing.

C. Webbing is so different from rope that special precautions and maintenance procedures must be taken.

D. Webbing is extremely durable so precautions and maintenance procedures are less important than with rope.

_____ 34. Which of the following parts of a rope is the free end that is used for hoisting, pulling, or belaying? (274)

A. Standing part

B. Working end

C. Running end

D. Bitter end

_____ 35. Which of the following parts of a rope is tied to the object being raised, lowered, or stabilized? (274)

A. Standing part

B. Working end

C. Running end

D. Laid end

36. All knots should be dressed after they are tied; that is, they should be: (274)
    A. tightened until snug with all slack removed.
    B. identified as complete with a nonpermanent marking device.
    C. left somewhat loose so a small amount of slack remains.
    D. left alone for several minutes, then tightened and the procedure repeated twice.

37. Which of the following statements about a rope's strength is MOST accurate? (274)
    A. The tighter the bend in a knot, the more strength is lost.
    B. The tighter the bend in a knot, the more strength is gained.
    C. The tightness of the bend in a knot has no affect on rope strength.
    D. The tightness of the bend can increase or decrease rope strength depending upon the knot.

38. Which of the following elements of a knot is formed by simply bending the rope back on itself while keeping the sides parallel? (275)
    A. Loop
    B. Bight
    C. Hitch
    D. Round turn

39. Which of the following knots is used in conjunction with other knots to eliminate the danger of the running end of the rope slipping back through a knot, causing the knot to fail? (275)
    A. Bowline
    B. Clove hitch
    C. Half-hitch
    D. Overhand safety knot

40. Which of the following knots is always used in conjunction with another knot and is particularly useful in stabilizing tall objects that are being hoisted? (276)
    A. Bowline
    B. Clove hitch
    C. Half-hitch
    D. Overhand safety knot

41. Which of the following knots is easily tied and untied and is good for forming a single loop that will not constrict the object it is placed around? (276)
    A. Bowline
    B. Clove hitch
    C. Half-hitch
    D. Overhand safety knot

_____ 42. Which of the following knots is primarily used to attach a rope to an object such as a pole, post, or hoseline but is not regarded as suitable for use in anchoring a life-safety rope? (276)

A. Bowline

B. Clove hitch

C. Half-hitch

D. Overhand safety knot

_____ 43. Which of the following knots is used primarily on life-safety rope to tie ropes of equal diameters together? (277)

A. Figure eight

B. Figure-eight bend

C. Figure eight on a bight

D. Figure-eight follow-through

_____ 44. Which of the following knots is used to secure a rope around an object and is essentially a figure eight on a bight that is around an object? (277)

A. Figure eight

B. Figure-eight bend

C. Figure-eight loop

D. Figure-eight follow-through

_____ 45. Which of the following types of knots is used for joining two ropes of unequal diameters or joining a rope and a chain, and is unlikely to slip when the rope is wet, but is not suitable in life-safety applications? (278)

A. Becket bend

B. Clove hitch

C. Water knot

D. Figure-eight on a bight

_____ 46. Which of the following types of knots is the preferred knot for joining two pieces of webbing or the ends of the same piece of rope when a loop is needed? (278)

A. Becket bend

B. Clove hitch

C. Water knot

D. Figure-eight on a bight

_____ 47. Which of the following rope hardware items is a metal snap link used to connect elements of a rescue system together? (278)

    A. Ascender

    B. Carabiner

    C. Brake bar rack

    D. Figure-eight plate

_____ 48. Which of the following rope hardware items is used to climb a vertical rope? (278)

    A. Ascender

    B. Carabiner

    C. Brake bar rack

    D. Figure-eight plate

_____ 49. Which of the following rope hardware items is used in rescue systems to change the direction of pull or create mechanical advantage? (278)

    A. Pulleys

    B. Carabiner

    C. Brake bar rack

    D. Figure-eight plate

_____ 50. Which of the following rope hardware items is used for rappelling or as a friction brake in lowering systems? (278)

    A. Pulleys

    B. Carabiner

    C. Ascender

    D. Figure-eight plate

_____ 51. Which of the following is a safety consideration when hoisting objects? (280)

    A. Work alone to minimize risks from falling objects.

    B. Use the hand-over-hand method to maintain control of the rope during a hoisting operation.

    C. Use the hand-under-hand method to maintain control of the rope during a hoisting operation.

    D. Use the double-handed method to maintain control of the rope during a hoisting operation.

_____ 52. Which of the following statements about hoisting hoselines is MOST accurate? (281)

    A. It is easier and safer to hoist a dry hoseline.

    B. It is easier and safer to hoist a charged hoseline.

    C. It is not recommended that hoselines be hoisted.

    D. It is just as easy to hoist a charged hoseline as a dry hoseline.

_____ 53. A clove hitch and two half-hitches are used to hoist a: (281)
   A. ladder.
   B. pike pole.
   C. power saw.
   D. portable fan.

_____ 54. Which of the following is a safety consideration when hoisting objects? (281)
   A. Never hoist objects weighing over ten pounds.
   B. Never hoist objects weighing over fifteen pounds.
   C. Do not hoist any objects that have sharp edges or points.
   D. Use a guide line to help control the object being hoisted.

_____ 55. Which of the following statements about rope rescue is MOST accurate? (282)
   A. Rope rescue is a technical skill that requires specialized training.
   B. Rope rescue can be done by any firefighter using any available rope.
   C. Rescue rope and appropriate hardware can be used to raise but not lower victims.
   D. Rescue rope and appropriate hardware can be used to lower but not raise victims.

_____ 56. Which of the following types of rescue harnesses is intended to be used for emergency escape with a load of up to 300 pounds (1.33 k/N)? (282)
   A. Class I harness
   B. Class II harness
   C. Class III harness
   D. Class IV harness

_____ 57. Which of the following types of rescue harnesses fastens around the waist and around the thighs or under the buttocks and is intended to be used for emergency escape with a load of up to 600 pounds (2.67 k/N)? (283)
   A. Class I harness
   B. Class II harness
   C. Class III harness
   D. Class IV harness

_____ 58. Which of the following types of rescue harnesses is also known as a full body harness and fastens around the waist, around the thighs or under the buttocks, and over the shoulders and is rated for loads of up to 600 pounds (2.67 k/N)? (283)
   A. Class I harness
   B. Class II harness
   C. Class III harness
   D. Class IV harness

_____ 1. Which of the following BEST describes incidents that involve the disentanglement and removal of victims from vehicles or machinery? (305)
   A. Rescue incidents
   B. Extrication incidents
   C. Offensive incidents
   D. Defensive incidents

_____ 2. Which of the following BEST describes incidents that involve the removal of victims from entrapment by fires, terrain features, structural collapse, elevation differences, and confined spaces? (305)
   A. Rescue incidents
   B. Extrication incidents
   C. Offensive incidents
   D. Defensive incidents

_____ 3. Which of the following items is the MOST important concern of emergency personnel performing search and rescue operations? (306)
   A. Safety
   B. Time
   C. Offensive operations
   D. Public relations

_____ 4. When should size-up be done during a search and rescue operation? (306)
   A. Only during the initial phase of the operation
   B. During the initial phase and throughout the operation
   C. Search and rescue operations do not have time for size-up
   D. During the initial phase and after the incident is terminated

_____ 5. During search and rescue operations, if backdraft conditions are apparent, attempt entry: (306)
   A. only after ventilation is accomplished.
   B. only after the incident is terminated.
   C. only after the fire is declared under control.
   D. only after master streams have been applied.

Firefighter I

_____ 6. What should firefighters do if a building fire has progressed to the point that viable victims are not likely to be found? (306)

    A. They should not enter the building.

    B. They should enter the building after back-up personnel arrive.

    C. They should enter the building only with charged hoselines.

    D. They should enter the building and look for victims using minimum personnel.

_____ 7. What should firefighters do when visibility is obscured during search and rescue operations in a building? (307)

    A. They should not enter the building.

    B. They should immediately leave the building.

    C. They should walk in the center or middle of the rooms.

    D. They should maintain contact with a wall, a hoseline, or a tagline.

_____ 8. When conducting search and rescue operations, firefighters should work: (307)

    A. alone.

    B. in teams of at least two.

    C. in teams of at least four.

    D. in teams of at least six.

_____ 9. If possible, when should the fire attack be started in an incident involving search and rescue operations? (308)

    A. Simultaneously with any interior search operations

    B. After interior search operations have been completed

    C. After interior search operations have been initiated

    D. Prior to any interior search operations being initiated

_____ 10. The two objectives of a building search are locating victims and: (309)

    A. extinguishing the fire.

    B. conserving property.

    C. assessing fire conditions.

    D. preserving evidence of arson.

_____ 11. Which of the following is a rapid but thorough search that is performed either before or during fire suppression operations? (309)

    A. Primary search

    B. Secondary search

    C. Rapid intervention

    D. Operational search

_____ 12. Which of the following is conducted after the fire is under control and the greatest hazards have been controlled? (309)
A. Primary search
B. Secondary search
C. Rapid intervention
D. Operational search

_____ 13. Which of the following is done to locate and rescue firefighters in distress? (309)
A. Primary search
B. Secondary search
C. Rapid intervention
D. Operational search

_____ 14. Where should firefighters start the search on the fire floor? (310)
A. As close to the fire as possible
B. As far away from the fire as possible
C. The area that is most easily accessible
D. The area that is most difficult to access

_____ 15. When is a dedicated search line MOST likely to be used? (312)
A. When searching areas with limited personnel
B. When searching large areas that have clear visibility
C. When searching small areas that have a limited number of rooms
D. When searching large or complex areas that are filled with smoke

_____ 16. Which of the following statements about a secondary search is MOST accurate? (314-315)
A. Speed is the most important factor in a secondary search.
B. The secondary search emphasizes thoroughness over speed.
C. Negative information found in the secondary search does not need to be relayed.
D. The secondary search is conducted by the same personnel who conducted the primary search.

_____ 17. When searching in multistory buildings, the most critical areas are the fire floor, the floor directly above the fire floor, and: (315)
A. the topmost floor.
B. the lowest floor.
C. the floor directly below the fire floor.
D. any floor that may possible contain occupants.

_____ 18. How should rescuers exit rooms that are being searched? (316)

    A. Through whatever exit they choose

    B. Through the most convenient exit available

    C. Through the same doorway they entered

    D. Through a different doorway than the one the entered

_____ 19. When using a marking system for searching, where should the marks be placed? (317)

    A. In the center of the wall or door

    B. At eye level on the wall or door

    C. On the upper third of the wall or door

    D. On the lower third of the wall or door

_____ 20. What should firefighters do if they find signs of a weakened floor/ceiling assembly when conducting a search? (318)

    A. Make a mental note of the signs.

    B. Immediately report the signs to Command.

    C. Disregard the signs and continue the search.

    D. Report the signs to command after exiting the building.

_____ 21. What should firefighters do if they realize that they are in imminent life-threatening danger? (320)

    A. Immediately transmit Mayday!

    B. Wait 1-3 minutes before transmitting Mayday!

    C. Wait 3-5 minutes before transmitting Mayday!

    D. Attempt to find a way out before transmitting Mayday!

_____ 22. What should a firefighter do if they are lost or disoriented and become exhausted or close to losing consciousness? (322)

    A. Lie flat in the middle of the room.

    B. Keep attempting to find a way out.

    C. Sit on the floor and lean against a wall.

    D. Stand up and brace against a wall or door.

_____ 23. Which of the following statements about a rapid intervention crew (RIC) is MOST accurate? (323)

    A. A RIC most be composed of at least four firefighters.

    B. RIC team members cannot have other fireground duties.

    C. RIC team members may be assigned other fireground duties.

    D. RIC team members do not have to have the same PPE as interior fire fighting crews.

_____ 24. Which of the following statements about radio transceivers is MOST accurate? (326)

    A. They can interfere with other on-scene radios.

    B. They have a range of approximately 100 feet (30 m).

    C. They have a range of approximately 50 feet (15 m).

    D. The radio transmission is blocked by walls, floor, and solid objects.

_____ 25. Which of the following is NOT a reason to move an injured victim before treatment is provided? (327)

    A. It is impossible to protect the accident scene.

    B. The accident scene is disturbing for the victim.

    C. There is fire or danger of fire in the immediate area.

    D. Explosives or other hazardous materials are involved.

_____ 26. Which of the following is the primary danger in moving a victim quickly? (328)

    A. The possibility of dropping the victim

    B. The possibility of aggravating a spinal injury

    C. The possibility of aggravating internal injuries

    D. The possibility of aggravating injuries to limbs

_____ 27. The cradle-in-arms lift/carry is BEST suited for carrying: (328)

    A. conscious adults.

    B. unconscious adults.

    C. conscious children or very small adults.

    D. unconscious children or very small adults.

_____ 28. Which of the following lift/carry is BEST suited for lifting a victim who is lying down? (329)

    A. Seat lift/carry

    B. Incline lift/carry

    C. Three-person lift/carry

    D. Cradle-in-arms lift/carry

_____ 29. Which of the following drags would be BEST suited for moving an unconscious victim up or down a stairway? (328)

    A. Incline drag

    B. Blanket drag

    C. Webbing drag

    D. Extremities drag

_____ 30. How many rescuers are required to immobilize a victim who is suspected of having a spinal injury on a long backboard? (330)
   A. One
   B. Two
   C. Three
   D. Four

_____ 31. Which of the following is a step-up transformer that converts a vehicle's 12- or 24-volt DC current into 110- or 220-volt AC current? (331)
   A. Inverter
   B. Generator
   C. Inductor
   D. Portable transformer

_____ 32. Which of the following is powered by small gasoline or diesel engines? (331)
   A. Inverter
   B. Generator
   C. Inductor
   D. Portable transformer

_____ 33. Which of the following is the most common power source used for emergency services? (331)
   A. Inverter
   B. Generator
   C. Inductor
   D. Portable transformer

_____ 34. Portable lights generally range from: (331)
   A. 75 to 300 watts.
   B. 100 to 250 watts.
   C. 300 to 1,000 watts.
   D. 1,000 to 5,000 watts.

_____ 35. Fixed lights are mounted to a vehicle and their main function is to: (332)
   A. provide lighting while the vehicle is driving.
   B. provide auxiliary lighting in small areas.
   C. provide lighting for adjacent neighborhoods.
   D. provide overall lighting of the emergency scene.

_____ 36. Which of the following may be used when multiple connections are needed at emergency scenes? (333)

    A. Adapters

    B. Receptacles

    C. Junction boxes

    D. Transformers

Rescue and Extrication

_____ 1. Which of the following should be done when replacing light bulbs? (334)
   A. Shut off the power to the light.
   B. Turn on the power to the light.
   C. Replace all bulbs every four to six months.
   D. Replace all bulbs if one bulb must be replaced.

_____ 2. Who should perform work on the generator portion of the power plant? (334)
   A. Any firefighter who uses the generator
   B. Personnel who have the time and aptitude
   C. Certified service personnel or a licensed electrician
   D. Any firefighter who has read the manufacturer's instructions

_____ 3. Which of the following powered hydraulic tools were the first powered hydraulic tools to become available to the fire/rescue service and has tips that may spread as much as 32 inches (800 mm) apart? (335)
   A. Shears
   B. Spreaders
   C. Extension rams
   D. Combination spreader/shears

_____ 4. Which of the following powered hydraulic tools is capable of cutting almost any metal object? (335)
   A. Shears
   B. Spreaders
   C. Extension rams
   D. Combination ram/spreaders

_____ 5. The spreading and cutting capabilities of the combination spreader/shears: (336)
   A. are the same as those of the individual units.
   B. are greater than those of the individual units.
   C. are somewhat less than those of the individual units.
   D. may be either greater or less than those of the individual units.

_____ 6. Which of the following powered hydraulic tools is designed primarily for straight pushing operations and can extend from a closed length of 3 feet (1 m) to an extended length of around 5 feet (1.5 m)? (336)

    A. Shears

    B. Spreaders

    C. Extension rams

    D. Combination spreader/shears

_____ 7. Which of the following is an advantage of manual hydraulic tools over powered hydraulic tools? (336)

    A. Operate more quickly

    B. Less labor-intensive

    C. Have broad range of operation

    D. Can be operated in areas inaccessible to powered units

_____ 8. Which of the following is a disadvantage of manual hydraulic tools when compared to powered hydraulic tools? (336)

    A. Heavy

    B. Relatively expensive

    C. Limited range of operation

    D. Cannot be used in many areas

_____ 9. Which of the following nonhydraulic jacks is also known as a high-lift jack and is the least stable of the various types of jacks? (338)

    A. Bar screw jack

    B. Post screw jack

    C. Trench screw jack

    D. Ratchet-lever jack

_____ 10. Which of the following nonhydraulic jacks is a heavy-duty device excellent for supporting collapsed structural members and has as its primary use holding an object in place? (338)

    A. Bar screw jack

    B. Post screw jack

    C. Trench screw jack

    D. Ratchet-lever jack

_____ 11. Which of the following nonhydraulic jacks is sometimes used to replace wooden cross braces in trench rescue applications? (338)
A. Bar screw jack
B. Post screw jack
C. Trench screw jack
D. Ratchet-lever jack

_____ 12. Which of the following is a characteristic of plastic cribbing? (339)
A. Less durable than wooden cribbing
B. Does not last as long as wooden cribbing
C. Relatively inexpensive compared to wood cribbing
D. Does not become contaminated by absorbing fuel, oil, and other substances

_____ 13. Which of the following pneumatic tools is often used in vehicle extrication situations and is good for cutting medium- to heavy-gauge sheet metal? (340)
A. Air chisel
B. Air knife
C. Impact tool
D. Whizzer saw

_____ 14. Which of the following pneumatic tools can blast away surface dirt with great efficiency? (341)
A. Air chisel
B. Air knife
C. Air vacuum
D. Whizzer saw

_____ 15. Which of the following pneumatic tools is often used for delicate cutting operations such as removing rings from swollen fingers? (342)
A. Air chisel
B. Air knife
C. Impact tool
D. Whizzer saw

_____ 16. Which of the following pneumatic tools is ideal for disassembling machinery in which a victim is entangled? (341)
A. Air chisel
B. Air knife
C. Impact tool
D. Whizzer saw

Firefighter II

_____ 17. Which of the following lifting/pulling tools is used to create an anchor point above a manhole or other opening to allow rescuers to be safely lowered into confined spaces? (342)

    A. Tripod

    B. Winch

    C. Pneumatic lifting bag

    D. Block and tackle system

_____ 18. Which of the following lifting/pulling tools is generally mounted behind the front bumper and is an excellent pulling tool? (342)

    A. Tripod

    B. Winch

    C. Pneumatic lifting bag

    D. Block and tackle system

_____ 19. Which of the following is a safety rule when using pneumatic lifting bags? (344-345)

    A. The bags should be inflated quickly.

    B. Bags should never be stacked more than three high.

    C. The bags should be positioned against a flexible surface.

    D. Rescuers should never work under a load supported only by air bags.

_____ 20. In most fire departments in the U.S. and Canada, the overwhelming majority of rescue incidents are: (346)

    A. water rescues.

    B. vehicle extrications.

    C. structural fire rescues.

    D. search and rescue operations.

_____ 21. What is the primary goal of stabilizing a vehicle? (350)

    A. To reduce damage that may be caused to the vehicle

    B. To make victims who are trapped more accessible

    C. To prevent sudden or unexpected movement of the vehicle

    D. To prevent other vehicles from colliding with the damaged vehicle

_____ 22. Which of the following is the most common method to prevent horizontal motion? (351)

    A. Cribbing

    B. Hydraulic jacks

    C. Pneumatic lifting bags

    D. Chock the vehicle's wheels

23. Which of the following is the final step in stabilizing a vehicle? (353)
    A. Chock the wheels.
    B. Tie off the vehicle with utility rope.
    C. Place caution tape or signs around the vehicle.
    D. Shut down the electrical power within the vehicle.

24. Restraint systems can remain operational for up to: (353)
    A. 5 minutes after the power is interrupted.
    B. 10 minutes after the power is interrupted.
    C. 20 minutes after the power is interrupted.
    D. 30 minutes after the power is interrupted.

25. Which of the following means that wounds have been dressed and bandaged, fractures have been splinted, and the patient's body has been immobilized to reduce the possibility of further injury? (356)
    A. Prepping
    B. Readying
    C. Bundling
    D. Packaging

26. Which of the following types of glass is manufactured from two sheets of glass that are bonded to a sheet of plastic sandwiched between them? (357)
    A. Lexan®
    B. Glazed glass
    C. Tempered glass
    D. Laminated safety glass

27. Which of the following types of glass is most commonly used in side windows and some rear windows? (357)
    A. Lexan®
    B. Glazed glass
    C. Tempered glass
    D. Laminated safety glass

28. Which of the following statements about removing windshields is MOST accurate? (357)
    A. Whenever possible, leave windshields intact.
    B. Whenever possible, windshields should be totally removed.
    C. Windshields are not part of the structural component of vehicles.
    D. Removing windshields is generally easier than removing side windows.

Firefighter II

_____ 29. Which of the following designations refers to the front post area where the front door is connected to the body of a vehicle? (359)

A. A-post
B. B-post
C. C-post
D. D-post

_____ 30. Which of the following patterns of collapse occurs when there is a simultaneous failure of exterior walls that results in the upper floors and the roof collapsing on top of each other? (362)

A. A-frame collapse
B. Pancake collapse
C. Lean-to collapse
D. Cantilever collapse

_____ 31. Which of the following patterns of collapse occurs when the outer walls remain intact and the upper floors and/or roof structure fail in the middle? (363)

A. A-frame collapse
B. Pancake collapse
C. V-shaped collapse
D. Cantilever collapse

_____ 32. Which of the following patterns of collapse occurs when one outer wall fails while the opposite wall remains intact? (363)

A. A-frame collapse
B. Pancake collapse
C. Lean-to collapse
D. Cantilever collapse

_____ 33. Which of the following patterns of collapse occurs when one or more walls of a multistory building collapse, leaving the floors attached to and supported by the remaining walls? (364)

A. A-frame collapse
B. Pancake collapse
C. Lean-to collapse
D. Cantilever collapse

_____ 34. Which of the following terms is a general term used to describe any of a variety of means by which unstable structures or parts of structures can be stabilized? (365)

A. Shoring
B. Leveling
C. Raising
D. Supporting

_____ 35. When performing a trench rescue, eliminate sources of vibration within: (366)
   A. 100 feet (30 m)
   B. 200 feet (60 m)
   C. 300 feet (100 m)
   D. 500 feet (150 m)

_____ 36. Which of the following statements about confined space rescue is MOST accurate? (366-368)
   A. Confined space rescue can be performed by any firefighter.
   B. Rescuers entering a confined space must wear a lifeline.
   C. Confined space rescues do not require the use of PPE or SCBA.
   D. The command post for confined space rescues is always inside the hot zone.

_____ 37. When involved with rescues involving electricity, who should be allowed to cut electrical wires? (369)
   A. Police personnel
   B. Licensed electricians
   C. Experienced firefighters
   D. Only power company personnel

_____ 38. When involved with rescues involving electricity, to avoid the hazard of being electrocuted rescuers should stay away from downed wires a distance equal to: (369)
   A. one-quarter span between poles.
   B. one-half span between poles.
   C. three-quarters span between poles.
   D. one span between poles.

_____ 39. When involved with water rescues which of the following methods involves extending a long-handled tool to the victim? (370)
   A. Go
   B. Row
   C. Throw
   D. Reach

_____ 40. When involved with water rescues which of the following methods involves using a boat to retrieve the victim? (370)
   A. Go
   B. Row
   C. Throw
   D. Reach

Firefighter II

_____ 41. When involved in ice rescues, which of the following methods is implemented when the victim is close to solid ground and responsive and able to hold onto an aid? (372)

A. Go

B. Row

C. Throw

D. Reach

_____ 42. Which of the following rescue situations is LEAST likely to be a true emergency? (373)

A. Ice rescue

B. Water rescue

C. Elevator rescue

D. Industrial extrication

_____ 1. Smaller versions of the pick-head and flat-head axe are: (397)
   A. not used in the fire service.
   B. used in forcible entry operations.
   C. used in technical rescue operations.
   D. used in overhaul and salvage operations.

_____ 2. Which of the following tools is the flat-head axe often paired with as a set and is referred to as irons? (398)
   A. Hux bar
   B. Rambar
   C. Claw tool
   D. Halligan bar

_____ 3. The continual advancement in security technology is: (398)
   A. limiting the use of the bolt cutter as a viable entry tool.
   B. increasing the use of the bolt cutter as a forcible entry tool.
   C. requiring bolt cutters to be replaced as use damages them.
   D. requiring operators to use bolt cutters in a more creative manner.

_____ 4. Which of the following tools is available in both powered and manual versions and is used to cut security bars on windows or doors? (398)
   A. Kelly tool
   B. Bolt cutters
   C. Rebar cutters
   D. Circular saw

_____ 5. Which of the following tools are also called exothermic cutting rods and are ultra-high temperature cutting devices capable of cutting through virtually any metallic, nonmetallic, or composite material? (400)
   A. Cutting flares
   B. Burning bars
   C. Plasma cutters
   D. Oxyacetylene cutting torches

6. Which of the following tools may be used to cut through heavy metal components but its use in the fire service is diminishing because of safety concerns? (399)
   A. Cutting flares
   B. Plasma cutters
   C. Oxygasoline cutting torches
   D. Oxyacetylene cutting torches

7. Which of the following tools is an ultra-high temperature metal-cutting device and requires a power supply as well as one of several compressed gases? (400)
   A. Burning bars
   B. Plasma cutters
   C. Cutting flares
   D. Oxygasoline cutting torces

8. Which of the following cutting tools uses a conventional cutting torch and dual-hose configuration and the fuel is delivered to the torch in liquid form? (400)
   A. Cutting flares
   B. Plasma cutters
   C. Oxygasoline cutting torches
   D. Oxyacetylene cutting torches

9. Which of the following is NOT a handsaw commonly used in the fire service? (401)
   A. Hacksaw
   B. Frame saw
   C. Keyhole saw
   D. Carpenter's handsaw

10. Which of the following power saws is ideal for cutting sheet metal body panels and structural components on vehicles when equipped with a metal-cutting blade? (402)
    A. Chain saw
    B. Rotary saw
    C. Circular saw
    D. Reciprocating saw

11. Which of the following power saws is used during natural disasters to clear trees and limbs from areas? (402)
    A. Chain saw
    B. Radial-arm saw
    C. Circular saw
    D. Reciprocating saw

_____ 12. Which of the following power saws is often used as a ventilation tool? (402)

A. Chain saw

B. Rotary saw

C. Circular saw

D. Reciprocating saw

_____ 13. Which of the following power saws is especially useful in situations where electrical power is readily available and heavier and bulkier power saws are too difficult to handle? (401)

A. Chain saw

B. Rotary saw

C. Circular saw

D. Reciprocating saw

_____ 14. Which of the following statements about the principle of the lever and fulcrum and prying tools is MOST accurate? (402)

A. The longer the handle, the greater the force produced.

B. The shorter the handle, the greater the force produced.

C. The longer the handle, the smaller the force produced.

D. The length of the handle does not affect the force produced.

_____ 15. Which of the following is MOST likely to be considered a disadvantage of manual hydraulic tools? (402)

A. Smaller

B. Lighter

C. Easier to carry

D. Labor intensive

_____ 16. Which of the following manually operated prying tools can have the tips of its forked and slightly curved head inserted between a door and the door frame and driven in by the sliding weight that surrounds the handle? (404)

A. Rambar

B. Crowbar

C. Flat bar

D. Claw tool

_____ 17. Which of the following hydraulic prying tools is designed primarily for vehicle extrication but can be used to force entry by placing it inside a door frame? (404)

A. Hydraulic ram

B. Hydraulic hux

C. Hydraulic Kelly tool

D. Hydraulic frame tool

_____ 18. Which of the following pushing/pulling tools can be used as a prying tool? (406)

   A. Clemens hook

   B. Plaster hook

   C. Roofman's hook

   D. San Francisco hook

_____ 19. Where should the firefighter be positioned when using a pike pole to break a window? (406)

   A. Upwind of the window and higher than the window

   B. Upwind of the window and lower than the window

   C. Downwind of the window and higher than the window

   D. Downwind of the window and lower than the window

_____ 20. When using striking tools, which of the following statements about eye protection is MOST accurate? (407)

   A. The helmet faceshield is sufficient by itself.

   B. No eye protection is required when using striking tools.

   C. Eye protection is optional and depends on the user's competence.

   D. Safety glasses or goggles in addition to the helmet faceshield must be worn.

_____ 21. Which of the following statements about prying tool safety is MOST accurate? (407-408)

   A. It is acceptable to use a cheater.

   B. Prying tools can be used as striking tools.

   C. If a job cannot be done with a particular tool, use a larger tool.

   D. It is acceptable to strike the handle of a pry bar with another tool.

_____ 22. When using a rotary saw, it is important to start all cuts at: (408)

   A. full revolutions per minute (rpm).

   B. 50% revolutions per minute (rpm).

   C. 75% revolutions per minute (rpm).

   D. zero revolutions per minute (rpm).

_____ 23. Power saws should NOT be used when working in: (408)

   A. outdoor areas.

   B. indoor areas with limited ventilation.

   C. a flammable atmosphere or near flammable liquids

   D. areas where self-contained breathing apparatus is required.

24. Which of the following statements about power saw safety is MOST accurate? (409)
    A. A dull saw is more likely to cause an accident than a sharp one.
    B. A sharp saw is more likely to cause an accident than a dull one.
    C. Saws should be either dull or sharp depending on the material being cut.
    D. Whether a saw is dull or sharp does not affect the likelihood of an accident.

25. When lifting heavy tools or other objects, always: (409)
    A. lift with back, not your legs.
    B. lift with your legs, not your back.
    C. lift with both your back and legs.
    D. lift with your shoulders and arms.

26. Which of the following is the BEST way to carry an axe? (409)
    A. Carry the axe on your shoulder.
    B. Carry the axe with the blade toward the body.
    C. Carry the axe with the blade away from the body.
    D. Carry the axe in the most comfortable position possible.

27. How should pike poles and hooks be carried when outside a structure? (410)
    A. With the tool head down and behind the body
    B. With the tool head up and behind the body
    C. With the tool head up in the air and ahead of the body
    D. With the tool head down, close to the ground, and ahead of the body

28. Never carry a running power tool more than: (411)
    A. 5 feet (1.5 m).
    B. 10 feet (3 m).
    C. 15 feet (4.5 m).
    D. 20 feet (6 m).

29. Which of the following is a guideline for the care and maintenance of wooden handles? (411)
    A. Paint the handle to help protect it.
    B. Varnish the handle to help protect it.
    C. Soak the handle in water to effectively clean it.
    D. Sand the handle if necessary to eliminate splinters.

Firefighter I

_____ 30. Which of the following is a guideline for the care and maintenance of forcible entry tools? (411-412)
   A. Oil unprotected metal surfaces lightly.
   B. Sharpen the blade on a bench grinder.
   C. Fiberglass handles should not be washed.
   D. Paint unprotected metal surfaces to protect them.

_____ 31. Power tools that are damaged or excessively worn should be: (413)
   A. marked and used with caution.
   B. used only for training purposes.
   C. given to departments that have difficulty finding funding.
   D. removed from service, tagged, and sent for repair or replacement.

_____ 32. What should firefighters always do before trying to force a door? (413)
   A. Make sure that the door is locked.
   B. Make sure no occupants are on the other side.
   C. See if any windows in the building are open.
   D. Yell for someone on the inside to open the door.

_____ 33. Which of the following is an easy way to recognize which way a door swings? (413)
   A. Look for the hinges
   B. Ask the building occupant
   C. Look at building plans or drawings
   D. Look at the construction material of the door itself

_____ 34. Which of the following can result when a door or window is opened? (413)
   A. Ventilation operations can be adversely affected.
   B. Forcible entry tools can be irreparably damaged.
   C. The building can be made more difficult to enter.
   D. Ventilation operations will always be more successful.

_____ 35. Most interior doors in newer residences are: (414)
   A. panel doors.
   B. ledge doors.
   C. solid core slab doors.
   D. hollow core slab doors.

_____ 36. Which of the following doors are usually exterior doors, heavy, and do not generally have windows or other openings? (414)

A. Panel doors

B. Ledge doors

C. Solid core slab doors

D. Hollow core slab doors

_____ 37. Which of the following doors are also known as batten doors and are found in warehouses, storerooms, barns, and sheds? (415)

A. Panel doors

B. Ledge doors

C. Solid core slab doors

D. Hollow core slab doors

_____ 38. Which of the following tools is often needed to force open a metal door that is set in a metal frame? (416)

A. Irons

B. Kelly tool

C. Power tools

D. Hand saws

_____ 39. Which of the following often makes sliding doors very heavy and expensive? (417)

A. Metal frame

B. Tempered glass

C. Reinforcements

D. Security measures

_____ 40. Which of the following mechanisms for locking revolving doors resembles a gate hook-and-eye assembly? (419)

A. Drop-arm type

B. Panic-proof type

C. Metal-braced type

D. Through-the-door type

_____ 41. Which of the following overhead doors is usually not too difficult to force and may be forced by prying upward at the bottom of the door with a strong prying tool? (419)

A. Roll-up

B. Tilt-slab

C. Sectional

D. Telescoping

42. Which of the following overhead doors is also called a sheet curtain door and is used as high-security service door? (420)
    A. Roll-up
    B. Tilt-slab
    C. Sectional
    D. Telescoping

43. Which of the following overhead doors consists of a number of interlocking, inverted U-shaped metal sections? (421)
    A. Roll-up
    B. Tilt-slab
    C. Sectional
    D. Telescoping

44. When overhead doors must be forced open, it is best to use a rotary saw to cut a square or rectangular opening about: (423)
    A. 3 feet (.9 m) high and half the width of the door.
    B. 2 feet (.6 m) high and one-quarter the width of the door.
    C. 6 feet (2 m) high and nearly the full width of the door.
    D. 10 feet (3 m) high and nearly the full width of the door.

45. Which of the following terms refers to movable assemblies designed to cover doorway openings in rated separation walls in the event of a fire in one part of a building? (423)
    A. Fire doors
    B. Curtain walls
    C. Separation panels
    D. Doorway partitions

46. Which of the following types of fire doors normally remain open and close only when the hold-open device releases the door because a fusible link has melted or due to activation of either a local smoke detector or a fire alarm system? (424)
    A. Self-closing
    B. Manual-closing
    C. Automatic-closing
    D. Secondary-closing

47. Which of the following locks is surface-mounted and often used as an add-on lock for doors that already have other types of locks? (426)
    A. Rim lock
    B. Padlock
    C. Bored lock
    D   Mortise lock

_____ 48. The key-in-knob lock is a: (426)
   A. rim lock.
   B. padlock.
   C. bored lock.
   D mortise lock.

_____ 49. Which of the following locks is a portable or detachable locking device? (427)
   A. Rim lock
   B. Padlock
   C. Bored lock
   D Mortise lock

_____ 50. Which of the following is the responsibility of the property owner for rapid-entry lockbox systems? (428)
   A. Proper mounting
   B. Locking the box
   C. Inspecting the completed installation
   D. Indicating the desired location for mounting

_____ 51. Which of the following tools is often chosen by departments for forcible entry because it is versatile and requires only one person to use it effectively? (428)
   A. Rambar
   B. Kelly tool
   C. Hux tool
   D. Claw tool

_____ 52. If breaking glass to gain access into a burning building, firefighters should wear SCBA and have: (429)
   A. a ladder ready to put into position.
   B. overhaul equipment ready to use.
   C. a charged hoseline in place, ready to attack.
   D. an uncharged hoseline in place, ready to activate.

_____ 53. The most common type of swinging door is one that swings at least: (429)
   A. 45 degrees to open and close.
   B. 90 degrees to open and close.
   C. 180 degrees to open and close.
   D. 360 degrees to open and close.

_____ 54. Which of the following doors has a horizontal wooden or steel security bar held in place across the door by wooden or metal stirrups attached to the inside of the door? (432)
   A. Doors with drop bars
   B. Double-swinging doors
   C. Doors with burglar bars
   D. Tempered plate glass doors

_____ 55. Which of the following doors are heavy, very expensive, difficult to break, and should be broken only as a last resort? (433)
   A. Doors with drop bars
   B. Double-swinging doors
   C. Doors with burglar bars
   D. Tempered plate glass doors

_____ 56. Which of the following is a device made of rigid, heavy-gauge wire and is designed to fit through the space between double-swinging doors equipped with panic hardware? (435)
   A. K-tool
   B. A-tool
   C. J-tool
   D. Shove knife

_____ 57. Which of the following is a device that was developed as a direct result of lock design changes such as collars or protective cone-shaped covers to prevent the lock cylinder from being unscrewed? (435)
   A. K-tool
   B. A-tool
   C. J-tool
   D. Shove knife

_____ 58. Which of the following is a wedge-shaped tool that will widen and break the shackles of padlocks and is inserted into the lock shackle and driven by a maul or flat-head axe until the padlock shackles break? (436)
   A. Bam-bam tool
   B. Hammerheaded pick
   C. Duck-billed lock breaker
   D. Hockey puck lock breaker

_____ 59. Which of the following tools uses a case-hardened screw that is screwed into the keyway of the padlock? (437)

    A. Bam-bam tool

    B. Hammerheaded pick

    C. Duck-billed lock breaker

    D. Hockey puck lock breaker

_____ 60. Which of the following is often the easiest and fastest way to cut chain-link fences? (438)

    A. Bolt cutters

    B. Rotary saw

    C. Chain saw

    D. Circular saw

_____ 61. Which of the following types of ladders can often be used to bridge masonry and ornamental fences? (438)

    A. Roof ladder

    B. Step ladder

    C. A-frame ladder

    D. Extension ladder

_____ 62. Which of the following is NOT one of the hazards of breaking the glass of the wrong window? (439)

    A. Disruption of ventilation efforts

    B. Intensification of fire growth

    C. Increasing fire load in one particular area

    D. Drawing fire to uninvolved sections of the building

_____ 63. Which of the following types of windows is secured by one or two thumb-operated locking devices located where the horizontal frame members of the top and bottom sashes meet? (440)

    A. Hinged windows

    B. Projected windows

    C. Jalousie windows

    D. Double-hung windows

_____ 64. Which of the following types of windows is opened with a small hand crank? (441)

    A. Hinged windows

    B. Projected windows

    C. Jalousie windows

    D. Double-hung windows

_____ 65. Which of the following types of windows consist of small sections about 4 inches (100 mm) high and as long as the window width? (442)

A. Hinged windows

B. Projected windows

C. Jalousie windows

D. Double-hung windows

_____ 66. Which of the following statements about Lexan® windows is MOST accurate? (443)

A. They are not any stronger than safety glass.

B. There is no clear way to identify them from other types of windows.

C. They can be easily broken with conventional forcible entry hand tools.

D. They are virtually impossible to break with conventional forcible entry hand tools.

_____ 67. Which of the following statements about security bars and screens is MOST accurate? (444)

A. They are generally easily forced open.

B. Power saws should not be used to force entry on security bars and screens.

C. They are difficult to force from the outside but easily opened from the inside.

D. They can present a significant barrier to entry for rescue and fire fighting.

_____ 68. Opening a hole in a wall is known as: (445)

A. pushing.

B. drilling.

C. breaching.

D. battering.

_____ 69. How can firefighters tell if interior wallboard has been reinforced? (446)

A. By visually looking at it

B. By asking building occupants

C. By identifying it during preincident planning surveys

D. By looking for the reinforcement stamp at the top and bottom

_____ 70. Which of the following is the BEST tool for breaching masonry walls? (446)

A. Kelly tool

B. Circular saw

C. Battering ram

D. Rotary saw

71.	Which of the following statements about breaching metal walls is MOST accurate? (448)
	A.	Power tools should not be used to breach metal walls.
	B.	Metal walls are not that common and rarely need breaching.
	C.	Conventional forcible entry tools will not work on metal walls.
	D.	Conventional forcible entry tools cut through the panels with relative ease.

72.	Subfloor construction is limited to either: (449)
	A.	wood or tile.
	B.	tile or ceramic.
	C.	wood or concrete.
	D.	concrete or ceramic.

73.	When cutting a wooden floor carpets and rugs should be: (450)
	A.	left in place.
	B.	made as flat as possible.
	C.	removed or rolled to one side.
	D.	wetted down with an extinguishing agent.

74.	Which of the following tools makes the neatest cuts in wooden flooring? (450)
	A.	Chain saw
	B.	Rotary saw
	C.	Circular saw
	D.	Drywall saw

75.	Which of the following is the BEST tool for breaching concrete floors? (450)
	A.	Kelly tool
	B.	Circular saw
	C.	Battering ram
	D.	Jackhammer

1. Which of the following parts of a ladder is the main structural member of a ladder supporting the rungs or rung blocks? (472)
   A. Beam
   B. Butt
   C. Bed section
   D. Truss block

2. Which of the following parts of a ladder is the lowest and widest section of an extension ladder? (472)
   A. Beam
   B. Fly section
   C. Bed section
   D. Truss block

3. Which of the following parts of a ladder is the upper section of extension or some combination ladders and is the section that moves? (472)
   A. Guides
   B. Fly section
   C. Bed section
   D. Main section

4. Which of the following parts of a ladder is the bottom end of the ladder and is placed on the ground or other supporting surface when the ladder is positioned? (472)
   A. Tip
   B. Butt
   C. Locks
   D. Stops

5. Which of the following parts of a ladder is the rope or cable used for hoisting and lowering the fly sections of an extension ladder? (473)
   A. Guides
   B. Pawls
   C. Tie rods
   D. Halyard

6. Which of the following parts of a ladder are curved metal devices installed near the top end of roof ladders to secure the ladder to the highest point on a peaked roof of a building? (473)
   A. Guides
   B. Pawls
   C. Hooks
   D. Tie rods

7. Which of the following parts of a ladder is the extreme top of a ladder? (475)
   A. Tip
   B. Butt
   C. Locks
   D. Stops

8. Which of the following parts of a ladder are metal rods extending from one beam to the other? (475)
   A. Guides
   B. Pawls
   C. Hooks
   D. Tie rods

9. Single ladders are most often identified by: (476)
   A. the overall length of the beams.
   B. the overall width of the rungs.
   C. the maximum weight limit of the ladder.
   D. the material that the ladder is constructed from.

10. Which of the following ladders is often used for interior attic access and has hinged rungs? (476)
    A. Roof ladder
    B. Folding ladder
    C. Pole ladder
    D. Pompier ladder

11. Which of the following is a single ladder equipped with folding hooks that provide a means of anchoring the ladder? (476)
    A. Roof ladder
    B. Folding ladder
    C. Pole ladder
    D. Pompier ladder

_____ 12. Which of the following ladders is adjustable in length? (476)
- A. Roof ladder
- B. Folding ladder
- C. Pompier ladder
- D. Extension ladder

_____ 13. Which of the following ladders is referred to as a scaling ladder and is used to climb from floor to floor, via exterior windows, on a multistory building? (478)
- A. Roof ladder
- B. Folding ladder
- C. Pompier ladder
- D. Combination ladder

_____ 14. Which of the following ladders is designed so that it may be used as a self-supporting step-ladder and as a single or extension ladder? (478)
- A. Roof ladder
- B. Folding ladder
- C. Pompier ladder
- D. Combination ladder

_____ 15. Which of the following ladder construction materials has the highest cost and is the heaviest per unit of length? (478)
- A. Wood
- B. Metal
- C. Plastic
- D. Fiberglass

_____ 16. Which of the following ladder construction materials has the widest range of sizes and is easiest to repair? (478)
- A. Wood
- B. Metal
- C. Plastic
- D. Fiberglass

_____ 17. Which of the following ladder construction materials is generally a poor conductor of electricity and can suddenly crack and fail when overloaded? (478)
- A. Wood
- B. Metal
- C. Plastic
- D. Fiberglass

_____ 18. Ladders should meet which of the following National Fire Protection Association standards? (478)

    A. NFPA® 1021

    B. NFPA® 1041

    C. NFPA® 1931

    D. NFPA® 1500

_____ 19. All ground ladders should be tested before being placed in service, after any use that exposes them to high heat or rough treatment, and: (478)

    A. weekly.

    B. monthly.

    C. annually.

    D. every three years.

_____ 20. Which of the following terms refers to keeping ladders in a state of usefulness or readiness? (478)

    A. Repair

    B. Restore

    C. Assemble

    D. Maintenance

_____ 21. Who should be capable of performing routine maintenance on ground ladders according to departmental SOP and the manufacturer's recommendations? (479)

    A. All firefighters

    B. Only truck company firefighters

    C. Only factory certified repair technicians

    D. Only trained ladder repair technicians

_____ 22. Ladders should be inspected regularly and cleaned: (479)

    A. after every use.

    B. every other week.

    C. after being used several times.

    D. at the beginning of every month.

_____ 23. Which of the following is a general maintenance guideline for ground ladders? (479)

    A. Ladders can be stored outside if they are relatively new.

    B. Ladders can be painted entirely for additional protection.

    C. Ladders should not be placed near the vehicle exhaust pipe.

    D. Ladders that get moisture on them should be allowed to air dry.

24. Which of the following statements about cleaning ladders is MOST accurate? (479)
    A. Ladders are constructed to be very durable so cleaning is not often needed.
    B. A hard bristle brush and high-pressure sprayer are needed to effectively clean ladders.
    C. Ladders can be effectively cleaned by running a dry towel over them to remove debris.
    D. A soft bristle brush and running water are the most effective tools for cleaning ladders.

25. According to NFPA® 1932 ladders should be inspected after each use and: (480)
    A. on a daily basis.
    B. on a weekly basis.
    C. on a monthly basis.
    D. every two years.

26. Which of the following refers to a label affixed to the ladder beam near the tip to provide a warning that the ladder has been subjected to excessive heat? (480)
    A. Service label
    B. Heat sensor label
    C. Flame detection label
    D. Temperature warning label

27. Which of the following should be checked for tightness on a ladder? (480)
    A. Beams
    B. Rungs
    C. Pulleys
    D. Ladder guides

28. Which of the following would MOST likely indicate exposure to heat on a wooden ladder? (480)
    A. Water damage
    B. Rounded shoes
    C. Dark streaks in the wood
    D. Darkening of the varnish

29. Which of the following is an item to check when inspecting extension ladders? (481)
    A. Pulleys should be difficult to turn.
    B. Staypole toggles should not move.
    C. Hook and finger should move in and out freely on pawl assemblies.
    D. Halyard cable should be loose when ladder is in the bedded position.

_____ 30. What should be done if discrepancies are found when inspecting ground ladders? (481)

    A. The ladder should be used with caution.

    B. The ladder should be used for training purposes only.

    C. The ladder should be immediately discarded and a new ladder purchased.

    D. The ladder should be removed from service until it can be repaired and tested.

_____ 31. When lifting ladders below the waist: (482)

    A. use leg muscles, not back or arm muscles.

    B. use arm and back muscles, not leg muscles.

    C. use shoulder and arm muscles, not back muscles.

    D. use all the muscles possible to help lift the ladder.

_____ 32. Ladders should not be raised to within _____ of electrical wires. (482)

    A. 3 feet (1 m)

    B. 5 feet (1.5 m)

    C. 8 feet (2.4 m)

    D. 10 feet (3 m)

_____ 33. Which of the following is the optimum climbing angle for ladders? (483)

    A. 45 degrees

    B. 60 degrees

    C. 75 degrees

    D. 90 degrees

_____ 34. When placing a ladder, the base of the ladder should be placed away from the building approximately _____ of the vertical distance from the ground to the point of contact with the wall. (483)

    A. one-quarter

    B. one-third

    C. one-half

    D. two-thirds

_____ 35. When rescue from a window opening is to be performed, where should the tip of the ladder be placed? (484)

    A. Just above the windowsill

    B. Just below the windowsill

    C. Even with the windowsill

    D. To the left of the windowsill

36. Who should give the command to lift a ladder when two or more firefighters are lifting a ladder? (487)
    A. A firefighter in the middle
    B. A firefighter at the butt position
    C. A firefighter at the tip position
    D. Any firefighter who speaks up first

37. How are ladders carried in most cases? (488)
    A. Butt forward
    B. Tip forward
    C. At a 75 degree angle
    D. At a 90 degree angle

38. Which of the following ladder carries is typically used on extension ladders up to 35 feet (11 m)? (488)
    A. One-firefighter low-shoulder carry
    B. One-firefighter high-shoulder carry
    C. Three-firefighter flat-shoulder carry
    D. Two-firefighter arm's length on-edge carry

39. Which of the following ladder carries is best performed with lightweight ladders and is based on the fact that the firefighters are positioned on the bed section side of the ladder when it is in the vertical position? (488)
    A. One-firefighter low-shoulder carry
    B. One-firefighter high-shoulder carry
    C. Three-firefighter flat-shoulder carry
    D. Two-firefighter arm's length on-edge carry

40. Which of the following personnel is the MOST logical to decide exact placement of a ground ladder? (490)
    A. Firefighter nearest the tip
    B. Firefighter nearest the butt
    C. Firefighter in the middle
    D. Firefighter observing the carry

41. Ladder placement guidelines include laddering at least how many points on different sides of the building? (491)
    A. Two
    B. Three
    C. Four
    D. Five

_____ 42. Where should you avoid placing ladders? (491)

    A. Near corners of the building

    B. Over openings such as windows and doors

    C. On the same side of the building as streets

    D. On the same side of the building as apparatus

_____ 43. Which of the following statements about ladder placement is MOST accurate? (493-494)

    A. Ladders can be placed on uneven terrain as long as a firefighter stabilizes it.

    B. Ladders should have an angle of inclination that is approximately 60 degrees.

    C. Ladders may be placed on top of sidewalk elevator trapdoors or sidewalk deadlights.

    D. Ladders should not be placed where they may come into contact with overhead obstructions.

_____ 44. When placing ladders, an easy way to determine the proper distance between the heel of the ladder and the building is to divide the working length of the ladder by: (494)

    A. 2.

    B. 3.

    C. 4.

    D. 6.

_____ 45. In general, all modern metal and fiberglass ladders are designed to be used with the: (496)

    A. fly in.

    B. fly out.

    C. fly locked in position.

    D. fly able to move in or out.

_____ 46. Once an extension ladder is resting against a building and before it is climbed, the excess halyard should be: (497)

    A. cut off.

    B. moved to one side of the ladder.

    C. wrapped around the beams of the ladder.

    D. tied to the ladder with a clove hitch and overhand safety.

_____ 47. Which of the following ladders can one firefighter safety raise? (498)

    A. Single ladders and small extension ladders

    B. Any ladder that weighs under 100 pounds (45 kg)

    C. Any ladder that weighs under 150 pounds (68 kg)

    D. Ladders that are made of fiberglass or metal, regardless of type

_____ 48. Whenever two or more firefighters are raising a ladder, who is responsible for determining whether the ladder will be raised parallel with or perpendicular to the building? (498)
   A. Firefighter at the tip end
   B. Firefighter at the butt end
   C. Firefighter in the middle
   D. Firefighter observing the raise

_____ 49. The two basic ways for two firefighters to raise a ladder are the beam raise and the: (498-499)
   A. flat raise.
   B. angle raise.
   C. vertical raise.
   D. push raise.

_____ 50. What must be done when an extension ladder is raised with the fly in the incorrect position for deployment? (501)
   A. It is necessary to pivot the ladder.
   B. It is necessary to lower and raise the ladder again.
   C. It is necessary to force the fly into the correct position.
   D. It is necessary to use the ladder with the fly in the incorrect position.

_____ 51. Which of the following statements about shifting raised ground ladders is MOST accurate? (501)
   A. Shifting a ladder that is in a vertical position should never be attempted.
   B. Shifting a ladder that is in a vertical position should be limited to short distances.
   C. Shifting a ladder that is in a vertical position can be done as far as necessary.
   D. Shifting a ladder that is in a vertical position should only be done as a last resort.

_____ 52. One method of heeling a ladder is for a firefighter to stand on the: (502)
   A. outside of the ladder and chock the butt end with one foot.
   B. inside of the ladder and chock the butt end with one foot.
   C. outside of the ladder and press the second rung with one foot.
   D. inside of the ladder and press the second rung with one foot.

_____ 53. Which of the following is recommended to prevent the ladder from slipping or pulling away from the building? (503)
   A. Tying in
   B. Tying down
   C. Hooking in
   D. Splicing down

_____ 54. Which of the following is a guideline for climbing ladders? (503)

A. Grasp the rungs with palms up.

B. Grasp the rungs with palms down.

C. Grasp the same rungs while climbing.

D. Progress upward using your arm muscles.

_____ 55. How many firefighters are needed to bring victims down a ground ladder? (505)

A. One

B. Two

C. Three

D. Four

_____ 56. Small children who must be brought down a ladder can be: (506)

A. cradled across the rescuer's arms.

B. placed over the rescuer's shoulder.

C. lowered by their arms to another firefighter.

D. lowered by their legs to another firefighter.

1. The outcome of combustion in a confined space in which gases tend to form into levels according to temperatures, with the hottest gases at the ceiling, is known as: (542)

    A. chill tier.
    B. heat stratus.
    C. thermal layering.
    D. temperature leveling

2. Which of the following statements regarding life safety and ventilation is MOST accurate? (543)

    A. Ventilation creates zero chance for flashover.
    B. Ventilation increases the likelihood of flashover and backdraft.
    C. Ventilation allows firefighters to locate unconscious victims faster.
    D. Ventilation increases the chance of firefighters receiving steam burns.

3. Which of the following is created when a ventilation opening is made in the upper portion of a building and air currents throughout the building are drawn in the direction of the opening? (544)

    A. Ceiling jets
    B. Smoke stack
    C. Mushrooming
    D. Chimney effect

4. What is known as the tendency of heat, smoke, and other products of combustion to rise until they encounter a horizontal obstruction, at which point they spread laterally? (544)

    A. Upward flow
    B. Smoke stack
    C. Mushrooming
    D. Chimney effect

5. When should ventilation occur? (544)

    A. When hoseline crews arrive
    B. When the RIC deems it necessary
    C. After the IC determines the number of personnel appropriate
    D. After hoseline crews are ready to move in and attack the fire

_____ 6. The transition between the growth and fully developed stages of fire is known as: (544)

A. backdraft.

B. flashover.

C. mushrooming.

D. deteriorating.

_____ 7. Firefighters must remain aware that ventilation: (546)

A. causes severe backdraft conditions.

B. can also increase the potential for flashover.

C. completely eradicates the potential for flashover.

D. does not affect the potential for flashover or backdraft.

_____ 8. Which of the following is NOT a sign of potential backdraft? (547)

A. Smoke-stained windows

B. Lack of pressurized smoke coming from small cracks

C. Little visible flame from the exterior of the building

D. Smoke puffing at intervals from the building (appearance of breathing)

_____ 9. Techniques that use convection currents to ventilate a structure without the use of fans are known as: (547)

A. forced ventilation.

B. typical ventilation.

C. natural ventilation.

D. unnatural ventilation.

_____ 10. Techniques that involve the use of fans or blowers to ventilate a structure are known as: (547)

A. forced ventilation.

B. natural ventilation.

C. essential ventilation.

D. cosmetic ventilation.

_____ 11. Which of the following statements about life safety hazards is MOST accurate? (548)

A. The first consideration is property damage.

B. Occupants tend to avoid taking refuge in their rooms.

C. Ventilation must be performed prior to search and rescue.

D. Ventilation may be performed prior to search and rescue.

_____ 12. Which of the following statements about visible smoke conditions is MOST accurate? (548-549)

A. Smoke only accompanies unusual forms of combustion.

B. Smoke may become dense if polyurethane foam is involved.

C. The combustion process becomes more efficient as burning progresses.

D. The makeup of smoke is uniform, regardless of the materials being burned.

_____ 13. Thermal or chemical decomposition of fuel because of heat that results in the lowered ignition temperature of a material is known as: (549)

A. pyrolysis.

B. flame point.

C. stack effect.

D. combustion trigger.

_____ 14. The phenomenon of a strong air draft moving from ground level to the roof level of a building is known as: (550)

A. pyrolysis.

B. ceiling jets.

C. stack effect.

D. mushrooming.

_____ 15. Which of the following statements about high-rise buildings is MOST accurate? (550-551)

A. The danger from heat and smoke is inconsequential.

B. Under some conditions, elevator shafts may be used for ventilation.

C. If only one stairwell penetrates the roof, it is impossible to use for ventilation.

D. The safest ventilation technique is to depressurize the stairways with negative pressure fans.

_____ 16. Which of the following statements about basements and windowless buildings is MOST accurate? (552-553)

A. Outside entrances to basements are always accessible.

B. Effective ventilation has no effect on the ease of accessing a basement.

C. Creating openings needed to ventilate a windowless building may delay the operation considerably.

D. Limiting the steam generated by fire fighting efforts before ventilation is accomplished is unimportant.

_____ 17. Fire extension through windows or other outside openings where flame extends to other exterior openings and enters upper floors is known as: (553)

A. lapping.

B. leveling.

C. upbuilding.

D. transporting.

_____ 18. Which of the following could be considered a rule of thumb for selecting the exact point at which to open a roof? (553)

A. Open at least 25 feet away from the fire.

B. Open as directly over the fire as possible.

C. Open as far away from the fire as possible.

D. Open over the fire only if two holes are possible.

_____ 19. What is vertical ventilation? (556)

A. Ventilating at the lowest point of a building through created openings

B. Ventilating at the lowest point of a building through existing openings

C. Ventilating at the highest point of a building through existing or created openings

D. Ventilating by channeling products of combustion sideways out of a structure

_____ 20. Which of the following factors does NOT affect the likelihood of roof collapse? (556)

A. Volume of fire

B. Type of construction

C. Number of floors below the roof

D. How long the fire has been burning

_____ 21. A straight ladder with folding hooks at the top end is a(n): (558)

A. roof ladder.

B. aerial ladder.

C. standard ladder.

D. extension ladder.

_____ 22. Which of the following statements about roof ladders is MOST accurate? (559)

A. They are intended for use on fire-weakened roofs.

B. They cannot prevent slipping from a slippery roof.

C. They are intended to prevent slipping from a steep roof.

D. They make the transport of equipment to the roof more difficult.

_____ 23. When ventilating a roof, firefighters should work in groups of at least: (560)

A. two.

B. three.

C. four.

D. five.

_____ 24. Which of the following statements about existing roof openings is MOST accurate? (560-561)

    A. Existing openings are rarely locked.

    B. Doors to existing openings should be blocked open or removed.

    C. Existing openings are usually in the best location for ventilation.

    D. Breaking glass in skylights is an unacceptable method of ventilation.

_____ 25. A single cut the width of the saw blade made in a roof to check for fire extension is known as a(n): (562)

    A. kerf cut.

    B. angle cut.

    C. louver cut.

    D. determination cut.

_____ 26. Which of the following statements about ventilating roofs is MOST accurate? (562)

    A. A square opening is hardest to cut.

    B. Several small openings are better than one large opening.

    C. Rotary saws are ill-suited for cutting ventilation openings.

    D. Ventilation openings should be made at the highest point on the roof.

_____ 27. A rectangular exit opening cut in a roof, allowing a section of roof deck to be tilted, is known as a(n): (562)

    A. tilt cut.

    B. kerf cut.

    C. angle cut.

    D. louver cut.

_____ 28. Which of the following statements about flat roofs is MOST accurate? (562-563)

    A. The flat roof must have a slight slope to facilitate drainage.

    B. The flat roof is rarely penetrated by chimneys or vent pipes.

    C. The age of the flat-roof construction is the main determining factor of what equipment will be necessary to create ventilation openings.

    D. The structural part of a flat roof is generally similar to the construction of a floor assembly consisting of joists covered with sheathing or decking.

_____ 29. A lightweight truss design noted by the curve of the top chord is known as a(n): (563)

    A. arc truss.

    B. range truss.

    C. bowstring truss.

    D. elongated truss.

_____ 30. Sheathing consisting of boards or planks set with a small space between them is known as: (564)
   A. skip sheathing.
   B. space sheathing.
   C. uniform sheathing.
   D. elongated sheathing.

_____ 31. Which of the following statements about arched roofs is MOST accurate? (564-565)
   A. Lamella roofs are supported by buttresses or tie rods or both.
   B. Roof ladders are recommended for ventilation operations on arched roofs.
   C. The attic space created by an arched roof exposes fire in progress quickly.
   D. Lamella arched roofs are made of relatively long boards of differing lengths.

_____ 32. A horizontal member between trusses that supports the roof is a: (565)
   A. rod.
   B. purlin.
   C. top hold.
   D. cockloft.

_____ 33. Which of the following is one of the two common types of concrete roofs? (565)
   A. Molded
   B. Die-cast
   C. Heavyweight
   D. Poured-in-place

_____ 34. Which of the following statements about metal roofs is MOST accurate? (566-567)
   A. Aluminum is usually covered with a roofing material.
   B. Corrugated galvanized sheet metal is impossible to pry from supports.
   C. Metal roofs on industrial buildings are often penetrated by roof openings such as skylights.
   D. Light-gauge cold-formed steel sheets are used primarily for the roofs of commercial buildings.

_____ 35. A defensive tactic that involves cutting an exit opening in the roof of a burning building and extending it from one wall to the other is known as: (567)
   A. cross ventilation.
   B. trench ventilation.
   C. horizontal ventilation.
   D. hydraulic ventilation.

36. Which of the following statements about conventional basement fire ventilation is MOST accurate? (567-568)

   A. Natural paths from the basement can be used to evacuate heat and smoke.

   B. Heat and smoke from basement fires generally spreads slowly upward into the building.

   C. The attic should be vented to remove residual smoke prior to confirming that the basement fire is extinguished.

   D. The likelihood of vertical extension of the fire will be increased by direct ventilation of the basement during fire attack.

37. What is a thermal column? (569)

   A. A vertical fire stream that cools the products of combustion

   B. A pocket of fire gases drawn horizontally out of the building

   C. An updraft of heated air, fire gases, and smoke directly above the involved fire area

   D. A phenomenon created when air currents throughout the building are drawn downward

38. Which of the following is a common factor that can reduce the effectiveness of vertical ventilation? (569)

   A. Coordinated window breaking

   B. Burn-through of the floor or a wall

   C. Fire streams not directed into ventilation openings

   D. Using elevated streams properly to cool the thermal column

39. What is the venting of heat, smoke, and gases through openings such as windows and doors? (570)

   A. Vertical ventilation

   B. Common ventilation

   C. Hydraulic ventilation

   D. Horizontal ventilation

40. The side or direction from which the wind is blowing is the: (570)

   A. flow side.

   B. impact side.

   C. leeward side.

   D. windward side.

41. The direction opposite from which the wind is blowing is the: (570)

   A. flow side.

   B. impact side.

   C. leeward side.

   D. windward side.

_____ 42. Which of the following statements regarding horizontal ventilation exposures is MOST accurate? (570-571)

    A. Heat and gases will not ignite eaves of the burning building.

    B. When setting up horizontal ventilations, firefighters only need to consider external exposures.

    C. There is a danger that the rising gases will ignite portions of the building above the exit point.

    D. In all cases, a building should be ventilated before charged hoselines are in place at the entry point.

_____ 43. Which of the following is an advantage of forced ventilation? (573)

    A. It does not require special equipment.

    B. It is not dependent upon a power source.

    C. It cannot cause a fire to intensify and spread.

    D. It does not allow for as much smoke damage.

_____ 44. Which of the following is a disadvantage of forced ventilation? (573)

    A. It increases smoke damage.

    B. It may cause a fire to spread.

    C. It reduces control of air flow.

    D. It slows the removal of contaminants.

_____ 45. A technique using smoke ejectors to develop artificial circulation and pull smoke out of a structure is known as: (574)

    A. non-ventilation.

    B. inter-ventilation.

    C. positive-pressure ventilation.

    D. negative-pressure ventilation.

_____ 46. The movement of smoke being blown out of a ventilation opening only to be drawn back inside by negative pressure is: (574)

    A. drafting.

    B. swinging.

    C. churning.

    D. billowing.

_____ 47. The method of ventilating a confined space by mechanically blowing fresh air into the space is known as: (575)

    A. non-ventilation

    B. inter-ventilation.

    C. positive-pressure ventilation.

    D. negative-pressure ventilation.

48. Which of the following is an action that should be taken to ensure an effective PPV operation? (577-578)

    A. Increase the number of exit openings.

    B. Create exit openings on the windward side of the building.

    C. Direct heat and smoke away from unburned areas.

    D. Send firefighters into the smoke-filled environment to set up PPV.

49. A method of ventilating a fire building by directing a fog stream of water out a window to increase air and smoke movement is known as: (578)

    A. natural ventilation.

    B. vertical ventilation.

    C. hydraulic ventilation.

    D. negative-pressure ventilation.

50. Which of the following is a disadvantage of hydraulic ventilation? (578)

    A. There will be a drain on the available water supply.

    B. The nozzle team cannot leave the area to replenish their air supply.

    C. There will be an increase in the amount of smoke damage within the structure.

    D. Firefighters operating the nozzle must remain out in the elements during the operation.

Chapter 12

Water Supply

_____ 1. Most fire hydrants are made of: (605)

    A. steel.

    B. PVC.

    C. copper.

    D. cast iron.

_____ 2. Closing a hydrant too fast may cause a sudden increase in water pressure known as: (605)

    A. water impact.

    B. pressure limit.

    C. water hammer.

    D. pressure maximum.

_____ 3. Which type of hydrant has a main valve located below the frost line that prevents water from entering the hydrant barrel? (605-606)

    A. Dry-barrel

    B. Wet-barrel

    C. Long-barrel

    D. Short-barrel

_____ 4. Which type of hydrant is installed in areas where prolonged periods of subfreezing weather are common? (605)

    A. Dry-barrel

    B. Wet-barrel

    C. Long-barrel

    D. Short-barrel

_____ 5. Which type of hydrant is usually installed in warmer climates where prolonged periods of subfreezing weather are uncommon? (607)

    A. Dry-barrel

    B. Wet-barrel

    C. Long-barrel

    D. Short-barrel

6. Which of the following statements about the hydrant barrel of a dry-barrel hydrant is MOST accurate? (606)
   A. It is usually empty from the top of the stem down to the main valve.
   B. It is usually filled from the top of the stem down to the main valve.
   C. It is usually closed from the top of the stem down to the main valve.
   D. It is usually cut off from the top of the stem down to the main valve.

7. Which type of hydrant has a horizontal compression-type valve at each outlet? (607)
   A. Dry-barrel
   B. Wet-barrel
   C. Long-barrel
   D. Short-barrel

8. When a dry-barrel hydrant is closed after use, the remaining water empties through a: (606)
   A. drain hole.
   B. drain plug.
   C. gate valve.
   D. butterfly valve.

9. Who usually makes decisions regarding location, spacing, and distribution of fire hydrants? (607)
   A. Fire inspectors
   B. Water engineers
   C. Fire department personnel
   D. Water department personnel

10. Which of the following is the MAXIMUM spacing of fire hydrants in high-value districts? (607)
    A. 100 feet (30 m)
    B. 200 feet (60 m)
    C. 300 feet (100 m)
    D. 400 feet (120 m)

11. Which of the following statements regarding hydrant location is MOST accurate? (607)
    A. One should be located at every intersection.
    B. One should be located at every other intersection.
    C. One should be located at every third intersection.
    D. One should be located at every fourth intersection.

_____ 12. Intermediate hydrants may be required where distances between intersections exceed: (607-608)
   A. 150 to 200 feet (45 to 60 m).
   B. 250 to 300 feet (75 to 100 m).
   C. 350 to 400 feet (105 to 120 m).
   D. 450 to 500 feet (135 to 150 m).

_____ 13. According to the NFPA®, which color hydrant indicates a flow of 1,500 gpm (5 680) L/min) or greater? (609)
   A. Red
   B. Green
   C. Orange
   D. Light blue

_____ 14. According to the NFPA®, a green hydrant indicates a flow of: (609)
   A. less than 500 gpm (1 900 L/min).
   B. 500 to 999 gpm (1 900 L/min to 3 780 L/min).
   C. 1,000 to 1,499 gpm (3 785 L/min to 5 675 L/min).
   D. 1,500 gpm (5 680 L/min) or greater.

_____ 15. According to the NFPA®, which color hydrant indicates a flow of less than 500 gpm (1 900 L/min)? (609)
   A. Red
   B. Green
   C. Orange
   D. Light blue

_____ 16. According to the NFPA®, an orange hydrant indicates a flow of: (609)
   A. less than 500 gpm (1 900 L/min).
   B. 500 to 999 gpm (1 900 L/min to 3 780 L/min).
   C. 1,000 to 1,499 gpm (3 785 L/min to 5 675 L/min).
   D. 1,500 gpm (5 680 L/min) or greater.

_____ 17. In most cities, the repair and maintenance of fire hydrants is the responsibility of the: (608)
   A. fire department.
   B. water department.
   C. highway department.
   D. loss-control agent.

_____ 18. Which of the following is NOT something to look for when inspecting fire hydrants? (608-609)

    A. Painted hydrants

    B. Type of property in area

    C. Damp ground or erosion surrounding the hydrant

    D. Insufficient clearance between outlets and the ground

_____ 19. Which of the following statements about fire hydrant testing is MOST accurate? (609)

    A. Fire hydrants should be tested on a quarterly basis.

    B. Fire hydrants should be tested on a bi-monthly basis.

    C. Fire hydrant testing is always performed by the fire department.

    D. Many departments are no longer responsible for the testing of hydrants.

_____ 20. How many outlet caps should be removed when conducting a flow test on a hydrant? (609)

    A. One

    B. Two

    C. Three

    D. All

_____ 21. After inspecting outlet caps during a flow test, replace all caps EXCEPT: (609)

    A. the top outlet cap.

    B. the bottom outlet cap.

    C. one 2½-inch (65 mm) cap.

    D. two 2½-inch (65 mm) caps.

_____ 22. To what should a cap-type pressure gauge be connected during a flow test? (609)

    A. The pumper

    B. An overflow unit

    C. A second hydrant nearby

    D. The hydrant being tested

_____ 23. What is drafting? (610)

    A. Acquiring water from a hydrant to supply a static source

    B. Acquiring water from a static source to supply a hydrant

    C. Acquiring water from a static source and transferring it into a pump

    D. Acquiring water from a pump and transferring it into a static source

_____ 24. A minimum of how much water is needed above and below a hard intake strainer for it to function properly? (611)
A. 12 inches (300 mm)
B. 24 inches (600 mm)
C. 36 inches (900 mm)
D. 48 inches (1 200 mm)

_____ 25. Which kind of strainers can draft water from more shallow sources? (611)
A. Intake
B. Drafting
C. Floating
D. Underground

_____ 26. Dry hydrants at static water sources are designed to supply at least how much water? (611)
A. 500 gpm (2 000 L/min)
B. 1,000 gpm (4 000 L/min)
C. 1,500 gpm (6 000 L/min)
D. 2,000 gpm (8 000 L/min)

_____ 27. Dry hydrants are often constructed of: (611)
A. steel.
B. copper.
C. cast iron.
D. fiberglass.

_____ 28. Which of the following is the definition of a water shuttle? (612)
A. Hauling water from a portable tank to the fire
B. Drawing water from a pumper to supply a hoseline
C. Hauling water from a supply source to portable tanks
D. Drawing water from a static source to supply a pumper

_____ 29. Water shuttles are recommended for distances greater than: (612)
A. ½ mile (0.8 km).
B. 1 mile (1.6 km).
C. 1½ mile (2.4 km).
D. 2 mile (3.2 km).

_____ 30. Which of the following is NOT a key component of a water shuttle? (612)
   A. Attack apparatus at the fire
   B. Fill apparatus at the fill site
   C. Remote tankers at the dump site
   D. Water tenders to haul water from the fill site to the dump site

_____ 31. Where is the dump site of a water shuttle generally located? (612)
   A. Near the fire or incident
   B. Near the static water source
   C. As close to the station as possible.
   D. Between the fill site and dump site

_____ 32. Portable tanks range from how many gallons (L) upward? (613)
   A. 250 (1 000)
   B. 500 (2 000)
   C. 750 (3 000)
   D. 1,000 (4 000)

_____ 33. What may portable tanks use to transfer water from one tank to another? (613)
   A. Drain devices
   B. Discharge hoses
   C. Jet siphon devices
   D. Registration hoses

_____ 34. According to NFPA® 1901, water tenders on level ground should be capable of dumping or filling at rates of at least: (615)
   A. 250 gpm (1 000 L/min).
   B. 500 gpm (2 000 L/min).
   C. 750 gpm (3 000 L/min).
   D. 1,000 gpm (4 000 L/min).

_____ 35. Which of the following may be used when the water source is close enough to the fire scene that water shuttles are not necessary? (616)
   A. Portable tanks
   B. Gravity dumps
   C. Relay pumping
   D. Jet siphon devices

_____ 1. Which of the following is a surface water supply? (594)

    A. River

    B. Water well

    C. Storage tank

    D. Water-producing spring

_____ 2. Which of the following is a groundwater supply? (594)

    A. Lake

    B. River

    C. Reservoir

    D. Water well

_____ 3. Which of the following methods of moving water is most often found in agriculture and industrial settings? (595)

    A. Gravity system

    B. Combination system

    C. Direct pumping system

    D. Indirect pumping system

_____ 4. Which of the following is a disadvantage of a direct pumping system? (595)

    A. Dependence on gravity

    B. Dependence on electricity

    C. Independence from piping

    D. Independence from pumps

_____ 5. Which of the following methods of moving water uses a primary water source located at a higher elevation than the distribution system and delivers water to the system without the use of pumps? (596)

    A. Gravity system

    B. Combination system

    C. Direct pumping system

    D. Indirect pumping system

_____ 6. Which method of moving water is used in the majority of communities in North America? (597)

   A. Gravity system

   B. Combination system

   C. Direct pumping system

   D. Indirect pumping system

_____ 7. Which method of moving water may not be affected by an extended power outage or pump failure? (597)

   A. Combination system

   B. Direct pumping system

   C. Water treatment system

   D. Indirect pumping system

_____ 8. Gravity pressure is adequate only when the primary water source is located more than: (596)

   A. 75 feet (25 m) lower than the lowest point in the water distribution system.

   B. 75 feet (25 m) higher than the highest point in the water distribution system.

   C. 100 feet (30 m) lower than the lowest point in the water distribution system.

   D. 100 feet (30 m) higher than the highest point in the water distribution system.

_____ 9. Which of the following is a chemical added by water treatment facilities to kill bacteria in the water? (597)

   A. Fluoride

   B. Chlorine

   C. Fluorine

   D. Ammonia

_____ 10. Which of the following is the MAIN concern for fire protection at water treatment facilities? (597)

   A. Low water pressure

   B. Damage to pipes and valves

   C. Disability of the facility's pumps

   D. Contaminated water distributed to the public

_____ 11. An uncontrolled release of chlorine can force an evacuation of the facility and areas: (598)

   A. upwind of it.

   B. upstream of it.

   C. downwind of it.

   D. downstream of it.

_____ 12. The network of underground pipes used in a water distribution system are often called: (598)

A. mains.

B. leverages.

C. pressurizers.

D. distributors.

_____ 13. The reduction in water pressure caused by water flowing through pipes is called: (598-599)

A. friction loss.

B. friction gain.

C. friction accumulation.

D. friction decomposition.

_____ 14. Which type of fire hydrant receives water from only one direction? (599)

A. Dry feed

B. Circulating feed

C. Open-end hydrant

D. Dead-end hydrant

_____ 15. Fire hydrants that receive water from more than one direction are said to have: (599)

A. dead ends.

B. knotted line.

C. circulating feed.

D. multiple distributors.

_____ 16. Which of the following is the distribution system that provides circulating feed from all directions? (599)

A. Grid system

B. Main system

C. Valve system

D. Water system

_____ 17. Which of the following are the large mains that convey large quantities of water to various points in the system for distribution to secondary feeders and smaller mains? (599)

A. Distributors

B. Water valves

C. Primary feeders

D. Secondary feeders

_____ 18. Which of the following is the network of intermediate-sized mains that subdivide the grid within the various loops of primary feeders and supply the distributors? (599)

A. Distributors

B. Water valves

C. Primary feeders

D. Secondary feeders

_____ 19. Which of the following is the grid arrangement of smaller mains serving individual fire hydrants and blocks of consumers? (599)

A. Distributors

B. Water valves

C. Primary feeders

D. Secondary feeders

_____ 20. What size should water mains be in residential areas? (600)

A. At least 4 inches (100 mm) in diameter

B. At least 6 inches (150 mm) in diameter

C. At least 8 inches (200 mm) in diameter

D. At least 12 inches (300 mm) in diameter

_____ 21. What size should water mains be in industrial areas? (600)

A. At least 6 inches (150 mm) in diameter

B. At least 8 inches (200 mm) in diameter

C. At least 10 inches (250 mm) in diameter

D. At least 12 inches (300 mm) in diameter

_____ 22. Spacing of cross-connecting water mains in a gridded water supply system should be: (600)

A. every 300 feet (90 m).

B. every 600 feet (180 m).

C. every 900 feet (270 m).

D. every 1,200 feet (360 m).

_____ 23. Which types of water main valves visually show the position of the gate or valve seat? (601)

A. Gate valves

B. Butterfly valves

C. Indicating valves

D. Nonindicating valves

_____ 24. Which types of water main valves are normally buried or installed in utility manholes? (601)

A. Indicating valves

B. Nonindicating valves

C. Post indicator valves

D. Outside stem and yoke valves

_____ 25. Which types of water main valves include a hollow metal post that houses the valve stem and has the words OPEN and SHUT printed on it? (601)

A. Gate valves

B. Butterfly valves

C. Post indicator valves

D. Outside stem and yoke valves

_____ 26. Which types of water main valves have a yoke on the outside with a threaded stem that opens or closes the gate inside the valve? (601)

A. Gate valves

B. Butterfly valves

C. Post indicator valves

D. Outside stem and yoke valves

_____ 27. Which types of water main valves are usually the nonrising stem type? (601)

A. Gate valves

B. Butterfly valves

C. Post indicator valves

D. Outside stem and yoke valve

_____ 28. Which types of water main valves are tight closing and rotate a valve disk 90 degrees from the fully open to the tight-shut position? (603)

A. Gate valves

B. Butterfly valves

C. Post indicator valves

D. Outside stem and yoke valves

_____ 29. Proper valve spacing is necessary so that no more than how many fire hydrants must be closed off while a break in a main is being repaired? (603)

A. 2

B. 3

C. 4

D. 5

Firefighter II

Firefighter II

_____ 30. Water mains can be made of: (603)

    A. lead.

    B. copper.

    C. fiberglass.

    D. asbestos cement.

_____ 31. What is pressure? (604)

    A. The stored potential energy

    B. The speed at which water is flowing

    C. The force that moves water through a pipe

    D. The amount of water flowing through a hose

_____ 32. In the fire service, pressure is most often measured in: (604)

    A. bars.

    B. newtons.

    C. kilograms per meter.

    D. pounds per square inch.

_____ 33. Which type of pressure can be measured with a pitot tube and gauge? (604)

    A. Flow pressure

    B. Static pressure

    C. Stored pressure

    D. Residual pressure

_____ 34. Which of the following is the normal pressure existing on a system before water is released from a hydrant? (604)

    A. Flow pressure

    B. Static pressure

    C. Residual pressure

    D. Common pressure

_____ 35. Which type of pressure provides an indication of the availability of additional water? (604-605)

    A. Flow pressure

    B. Static pressure

    C. Stored pressure

    D. Residual pressure

36. Which of the following is the pressure created by the velocity of water coming from a discharge opening? (604)
    A. Flow pressure
    B. Static pressure
    C. Residual pressure
    D. Common pressure

37. Which of the following represents the pressure left in the distribution system at a specific location when water is flowing? (604)
    A. Flow pressure
    B. Static pressure
    C. Residual pressure
    D. Common pressure

1. The size of a fire hose refers to its: (633)
   A. inside diameter.
   B. outside diameter.
   C. longest section length.
   D. shortest section length.

2. Which of the following types of intake hose is used to transfer water from a pressurized water source to the pump intake? (633)
   A. Soft intake hose
   B. Hard intake hose
   C. Static intake hose
   D. Dynamic intake hose

3. Which of the following types of intake hose is used primarily to draft water from a static source? (633)
   A. Soft intake hose
   B. Hard intake hose
   C. Static intake hose
   D. Dynamic intake hose

4. Which of the following is NOT a recommended practice to avoid mechanical damage to fire hose? (634)
   A. Avoid excessive pump pressure on hoselines.
   B. Open and close nozzles, valves, and hydrants quickly.
   C. Avoid laying or pulling hose over rough, sharp edges or objects.
   D. Change position of folds in hose when reloading it on apparatus.

5. Which of the following is a guideline for preventing hose liner dehydration? (635)
   A. Use hot air for mechanical drying.
   B. Roll dry hose in a straight roll for storage.
   C. Lay fire hose on hot pavement to facilitate drying.
   D. Keep the outside of woven-jacket fire hose wet when not in use.

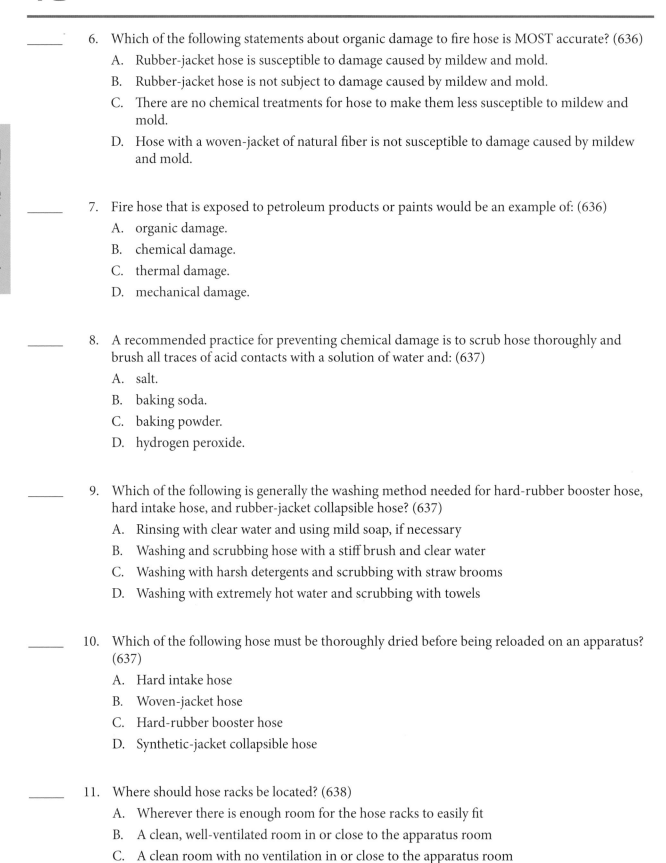

6. Which of the following statements about organic damage to fire hose is MOST accurate? (636)
   A. Rubber-jacket hose is susceptible to damage caused by mildew and mold.
   B. Rubber-jacket hose is not subject to damage caused by mildew and mold.
   C. There are no chemical treatments for hose to make them less susceptible to mildew and mold.
   D. Hose with a woven-jacket of natural fiber is not susceptible to damage caused by mildew and mold.

7. Fire hose that is exposed to petroleum products or paints would be an example of: (636)
   A. organic damage.
   B. chemical damage.
   C. thermal damage.
   D. mechanical damage.

8. A recommended practice for preventing chemical damage is to scrub hose thoroughly and brush all traces of acid contacts with a solution of water and: (637)
   A. salt.
   B. baking soda.
   C. baking powder.
   D. hydrogen peroxide.

9. Which of the following is generally the washing method needed for hard-rubber booster hose, hard intake hose, and rubber-jacket collapsible hose? (637)
   A. Rinsing with clear water and using mild soap, if necessary
   B. Washing and scrubbing hose with a stiff brush and clear water
   C. Washing with harsh detergents and scrubbing with straw brooms
   D. Washing with extremely hot water and scrubbing with towels

10. Which of the following hose must be thoroughly dried before being reloaded on an apparatus? (637)
    A. Hard intake hose
    B. Woven-jacket hose
    C. Hard-rubber booster hose
    D. Synthetic-jacket collapsible hose

11. Where should hose racks be located? (638)
    A. Wherever there is enough room for the hose racks to easily fit
    B. A clean, well-ventilated room in or close to the apparatus room
    C. A clean room with no ventilation in or close to the apparatus room
    D. A clean room that is separate and not easily accessible from other rooms in the fire station.

12. Which of the following types of couplings consists of a male coupling with external threads and a female coupling with internal threads? (639)
    A. Storz couplings
    B. Sexless couplings
    C. Threaded couplings
    D. Nonthreaded couplings

13. The portion of the threaded coupling that serves as the point of attachment to the hose is called the: (640)
    A. shank.
    B. spanner.
    C. rocker.
    D. screw.

14. Booster hose normally has couplings with: (640)
    A. pin lugs.
    B. rocker lugs.
    C. recessed lugs.
    D. double lugs.

15. The majority of new threaded couplings have rounded: (640)
    A. pin lugs.
    B. rocker lugs.
    C. recessed lugs.
    D. double lugs.

16. Which of the following refers to a special cut at the beginning of the thread on a hose coupling that provides positive identification of the first thread to eliminate cross-threading? (641)
    A. Kelly cut
    B. Higbee cut
    C. Locator notch
    D. Recessed cut

17. Which of the following statements about Storz couplings is MOST accurate? (641)
    A. Storz couplings have distinct male and female components.
    B. All Storz couplings of the same size are identical and may be connected to each other.
    C. Storz couplings are color-coded to identify which couplings can be connected to each other.
    D. Storz couplings of the same size are not necessarily identical depending on the manufacturer.

18. Which of the following is used to make the connection watertight when female and male ends are connected on threaded couplings? (642)
    A. Swivel gasket
    B. Recessed gasket
    C. Locking gasket
    D. Expansion-ring gasket

19. Which of the following is NOT a guideline for the care of fire hose couplings? (642)
    A. Drag couplings only on soft ground.
    B. Do not permit vehicles to run over fire hose.
    C. Inspect couplings when hose is washed and dried.
    D. Remove the gasket and twist the swivel in warm, soapy water.

20. Which of the following statements about hose appliances and hose tools is MOST accurate? (643)
    A. Water flows through both hose appliances and tools.
    B. Water flows through appliances but not through tools.
    C. Water flows through tools but not through appliances.
    D. Water flows through neither hose appliances nor tools.

21. Which of the following valves is used to control the flow from a hydrant and has a baffle that is moved by a handle and screw arrangement? (643)
    A. Ball valve
    B. Gate valve
    C. Clapper valve
    D. Butterfly valve

22. Which of the following valves is used on large pump intakes and incorporates a flat baffle that turns 90 degrees? (643)
    A. Ball valve
    B. Gate valve
    C. Clapper valve
    D. Butterfly valve

23. Which of the following valves is used in siamese appliances to allow water to flow in one direction only? (643)
    A. Ball valve
    B. Gate valve
    C. Clapper valve
    D. Butterfly valve

_____ 24. Which of the following appliances are used when supplying ladder pipes that are not equipped with a permanent waterway? (644)

A. Wye appliances

B. Hydrant valves

C. Siamese appliances

D. Water thief appliances

_____ 25. Which of the following appliances are most often used in wildland fire fighting operations? (644)

A. Wye appliances

B. Hydrant valves

C. Siamese appliances

D. Water thief appliances

_____ 26. Which of the following appliances are used when a forward lay is made from a low-pressure hydrant to the fire scene? (646)

A. Wye appliances

B. Hydrant valves

C. Siamese appliances

D. Water thief appliances

_____ 27. Which of the following terms refers to an adapter used to attach a smaller hose to a larger hose? (647)

A. Elbow

B. Hose cap

C. Hose plug

D. Reducer

_____ 28. Which of the following fittings provide support for intake or discharge hose at the pumping apparatus? (647)

A. Elbows

B. Hose caps

C. Hose plugs

D. Reducers

_____ 29. Which of the following are devices attached to the drafting end of a hard intake to keep debris from entering the fire pump? (648)

A. Elbows

B. Hose caps

C. Hose plugs

D. Intake strainers

_____ 30. Which of the following hose tools prevents damage from hose being dragged over sharp corners? (649)
A. Hose clamp
B. Hose chain
C. Hose roller
D. Hose jacket

_____ 31. Which of the following hose tools can be used to stop the flow of water in a hoseline? (649)
A. Hose clamp
B. Hose chain
C. Hose roller
D. Hose jacket

_____ 32. Which of the following hose tools can be used to connect hose with mismatched or damaged screw-thread couplings? (649)
A. Hose clamp
B. Hose chain
C. Hose roller
D. Hose jacket

_____ 33. Which of the following tools is used primarily to remove caps from fire hydrant outlets and to open fire hydrant valves? (651)
A. Hose bridge
B. Rubber mallet
C. Hydrant wrench
D. Spanner wrench

_____ 34. Which of the following tools is used primarily to tighten or loosen hose couplings? (651)
A. Hose bridge
B. Hose clamp
C. Hydrant wrench
D. Spanner wrench

_____ 35. Which of the following should be used wherever a hoseline is laid across a street or other area where it may be run over? (651)
A. Hose bridge
B. Chafing block
C. Hose chain
D. Hose strap

36. Which of the following is used to protect fire hose where the hose is subjected to rubbing from vibrations? (652)
    A. Hose bridge
    B. Chafing block
    C. Hose chain
    D. Hose strap

37. Which of the following is the simplest of all hose rolls? (653)
    A. Straight roll
    B. Donut roll
    C. Twin donut roll
    D. Self-locking twin donut roll

38. Which of the following rolls has the purpose of creating a compact roll that can be easily transported and carried for special applications such as high-rise operations? (653)
    A. Straight roll
    B. Donut roll
    C. Twin donut roll
    D. Double straight roll

39. Which of the following is a guideline for loading hose? (656)
    A. Pack hose as tightly as possible.
    B. Tighten couplings by using wrenches.
    C. Check gaskets and swivel before connecting any coupling.
    D. Load large-diameter hose with all couplings near the back of the bed.

40. Which of the following hose loads results in an arrangement of fire hose in a hose bed or compartment in which the hose lies on edge with the folds adjacent to each other? (657)
    A. Flat hose load
    B. Straight hose load
    C. Horseshoe hose load
    D. Accordion hose load

41. Which of the following hose loads is the easiest to load? (658)
    A. Flat hose load
    B. Straight hose load
    C. Horseshoe hose load
    D. Accordion hose load

_____ 42. Which of the following hose loads is best suited to large-diameter hose? (658)

    A. Flat hose load

    B. Straight hose load

    C. Horseshoe hose load

    D. Accordion hose load

_____ 43. Which of the following hose load finishes is designed to provide an adequate amount of hose at the scene for initial fire attack? (659)

    A. Straight finish

    B. Secondary finish

    C. Skid load finish

    D. Dutchman finish

_____ 44. Which of the following hose load finishes is designed to facilitate making a hydrant connection? (659)

    A. Straight finish

    B. Secondary finish

    C. Skid load finish

    D. Dutchman finish

_____ 45. Which of the following hose loads is adaptable for varying widths of hose beds and is often used in transverse beds? (662)

    A. Minuteman load

    B. Double layer load

    C. Triple layer load

    D. Preconnected flat load

_____ 46. Which of the following hose loads is designed to be pulled and advanced by one person and has the primary advantage of being carried on the shoulder? (663)

    A. Minuteman load

    B. Double layer load

    C. Triple layer load

    D. Preconnected flat load

_____ 47. Which of the following statements about booster lines is MOST accurate? (663)

    A. Booster lines are used for interior fire fighting operations.

    B. Booster lines are not appropriate for interior fire fighting operations.

    C. Booster hose reels are always mounted in the same location on all apparatus.

    D. Booster hose is used when additional hose is needed on high-intensity fires.

48. Supply hose with threaded couplings is usually loaded for a: (664)
    A. split lay.
    B. forward lay.
    C. reverse lay.
    D. combination lay.

49. In which of the following hose lays is hose laid from the water source to the fire? (664)
    A. Split lay
    B. Forward lay
    C. Reverse lay
    D. Combination lay

50. In which of the following hose lays is hose laid from the fire to the water source? (666)
    A. Split lay
    B. Forward lay
    C. Reverse lay
    D. Double lay

51. Which of the following hose lays is deployed by two pumpers, one making a forward lay and one making a reverse lay from the same point? (670)
    A. Split lay
    B. Forward lay
    C. Reverse lay
    D. Double lay

52. Which of the following hose loads is intended to be deployed without dragging any hose on the ground and the hose is flaked off the top of the shoulder as the firefighter advances toward the fire? (672)
    A. Minuteman load
    B. Triple layer load
    C. Double layer load
    D. Preconnected flat load

53. Which of the following is NOT a guideline for advancing hose into a burning structure? (673)
    A. Always check for and remove kinks from the line.
    B. Bleed air from charged hoselines before entering the building or fire area.
    C. Chock self-closing doors open to keep the line from being pinched by the door.
    D. Position the nozzle operator and all members of the hose team on alternating sides of the hoseline.

54. Which of the following statements about advancing hoseline is MOST accurate? (673)
    A. It is easier to advance charged hoseline up stairways.
    B. It is easier to advance uncharged hoseline up stairways.
    C. Advancing hoselines down a stairway is always much easier.
    D. Advancing charged and uncharged hoselines is the same as far as difficulty.

55. Which of the following statements about advancing hose up a ladder is MOST accurate? (675)
    A. Advancing fire hose up a ladder is easier and safer with a charged line.
    B. Advancing fire hose up a ladder is easier and safer with an uncharged line.
    C. It does not matter whether the line is charged or uncharged when advancing fire hose up a ladder.
    D. It is easier to advance an uncharged line up a ladder, but safer to advance a charged line up a ladder.

56. Which of the following is the safest way to control a loose hoseline? (677)
    A. Run over the hose with an apparatus tire.
    B. Put a kink in the hose at a point away from the break.
    C. Apply a hose clamp at a stationary point in the hoseline.
    D. Close a valve at the pump or hydrant to turn off the flow of water.

57. How many additional sections of hose should be used to replace any one bad section of hose when replacing burst sections? (678)
    A. One
    B. Two
    C. Three
    D. Four

58. Whenever one firefighter is required to operate a small hose and nozzle, the hoseline should be straight for at least _____ behind the nozzle. (678)
    A. 2 feet (0.6 m)
    B. 4 feet (1.2 m)
    C. 8 feet (2.4 m)
    D. 10 feet (3 m)

59. Except for overhaul or for very small outdoor nuisance fires, what is the minimum number of firefighters required for handling any attack line? (678)
    A. Two
    B. Three
    C. Four
    D. Five

_____ 60. When two firefighters are assigned to handle a large handline, the backup firefighter must serve as an anchor at a position: (679)

A. about 3 feet (1 m) behind the nozzle operator.

B. about 3 feet (1 m) in front of the nozzle operator.

C. about 6 feet (1.8 m) behind the nozzle operator.

D. about 10 feet (3 m) behind the nozzle operator.

_____ 1. When referring to hose appliances and hose tools, water flows through: (643)

    A. both hose appliances and tools.

    B. tools but not through appliances.

    C. appliances but not through tools.

    D. neither hose appliances nor tools.

_____ 2. Which of the following valves is used in pumper discharges and gated wyes and is open when the handle is in line with the hose and closed when it is at a right angle to the hose? (643)

    A. Ball valve

    B. Gate valve

    C. Clapper valve

    D. Butterfly valve

_____ 3. A _____ valve is used to control the flow from a hydrant and has a baffle that is moved by a handle and screw arrangement. (643)

    A. ball

    B. gate

    C. clapper

    D. butterfly

_____ 4. A _____ valve is used on large pump intakes and incorporates a flat baffle that turns 90 degrees. (643)

    A. ball

    B. gate

    C. clapper

    D. butterfly

_____ 5. Which of the following valves prevents water from flowing out of unused ports when one intake hose is connected and charged before the addition of more hose? (643)

    A. Ball valve

    B. Gate valve

    C. Clapper valve

    D. Butterfly valve

_____ 6. Which of the following appliances always have a single female inlet connection and two male outlets and are used to divide a single hoseline into two or more lines? (643)
   A. Wye appliances
   B. Hydrant valves
   C. Siamese appliances
   D. Water thief appliances

_____ 7. Which of the following appliances usually consist of two female inlets and a single male outlet and are used to combine two or more hoselines into one? (644)
   A. Wye appliances
   B. Hydrant valves
   C. Siamese appliances
   D. Water thief appliances

_____ 8. Appliances that are often used in wildland fire fighting operations are: (644)
   A. wye appliances.
   B. hydrant valves.
   C. siamese appliances.
   D. water thief appliances.

_____ 9. Which of the following appliances are used when fire fighting operations require that water be distributed at various points along the main supply line? (645)
   A. Wye appliances
   B. Hydrant valves
   C. Siamese appliances
   D. LDH water thief

_____ 10. Which of the following appliances allow the original supply line to be connected to the hydrant and charged before the arrival of another pumper at the hydrant? (646)
   A. Wye appliances
   B. Hydrant valves
   C. Siamese appliances
   D. Water thief appliances

_____ 11. The threads on pump male discharge outlets are protected with: (647)
   A. elbows.
   B. reducers.
   C. hose caps.
   D. hose plugs.

12. Which of the following is used to connect a smaller hoseline to the end of a larger one? (647)
    A. Elbow
    B. Hose cap
    C. Adapter
    D. Reducer

13. Fittings that provide support for intake or discharge hose at the pumping apparatus are known as: (647)
    A. reducers.
    B. elbows.
    C. hose caps.
    D. hose plugs.

14. Devices that are attached to the drafting end of a hard intake to keep debris from entering the fire pump are: (648)
    A. elbows.
    B. catchalls.
    C. intake filters.
    D. intake strainers.

15. Which of the following hose tools prevents damage from hose being dragged over sharp corners? (649)
    A. Hose clamp
    B. Hose strap
    C. Hose roller
    D. Hose jacket

16. Which of the following hose tools consists of a hinged two-piece metal cylinder and is installed at the point of rupture of a hoseline? (649)
    A. Hose clamp
    B. Hose chain
    C. Hose roller
    D. Hose jacket

17. Which of the following hose tools would be used to allow extension of a hoseline without shutting down the water supply? (649)
    A. Hose clamp
    B. Hose chain
    C. Hose roller
    D. Hose jacket

13

18. General rules for using hose clamps include applying the hose clamp at least: (650)
    A. 5 feet (1.5 m) behind the apparatus.
    B. 10 feet (3 m) behind the apparatus.
    C. 15 feet (4.5 m) behind the apparatus.
    D. 20 feet (6 m) behind the apparatus.

19. The hose clamp should be applied within _____ from the coupling on the incoming water side. (650)
    A. 5 feet (1.5 m)
    B. 10 feet (3 m)
    C. 15 feet (5 m)
    D. 20 feet (6 m)

20. Which of the following is a specially designed tool used to open or close a hydrant and to remove hydrant caps? (651)
    A. Hose bridge
    B. Rubber mallet
    C. Hydrant wrench
    D. Spanner wrench

21. The _____ is used primarily to tighten or loosen hose couplings. (651)
    A. hose ramp
    B. service wrench
    C. hydrant wrench
    D. spanner wrench

22. Which of the following tools is sometimes used to strike the lugs to tighten or loosen intake hose couplings? (651)
    A. Hose bridge
    B. Rubber mallet
    C. Hydrant wrench
    D. Spanner wrench

23. Which of the following can be positioned over small spills to keep hoselines from being contaminated? (651)
    A. Hose bridge
    B. Chafing block
    C. Hose chain
    D. Hose strap

24. Which of the following is particularly useful where intake hose comes in contact with pavement or curbs? (652)
    A. Hose bridge
    B. Hose chain
    C. Hose strap
    D. Chafing block

25. Which of the following provides a more secure means to handle pressurized hose when applying water? (652)
    A. Hose strap
    B. Hose ramp
    C. Hose bridge
    D. Chafing block

26. Which of the following refers to preservice tests on fire apparatus or equipment performed at the factory or after delivery to assure the purchaser that the apparatus or equipment meets bid specifications? (680)
    A. Service testing
    B. Acceptance testing
    C. Assurance testing
    D. Verification testing

27. Which of the following refers to a series of tests performed on apparatus and equipment in order to ensure operational readiness of the unit? (680)
    A. Service testing
    B. Acceptance testing
    C. Assurance testing
    D. Verification testing

28. Fire department personnel should NOT attempt: (680)
    A. service testing.
    B. acceptance testing.
    C. assurance testing.
    D. verification testing.

29. Fire hose should undergo service testing after being repaired, after being run over by a vehicle, and: (680)
    A. weekly.
    B. monthly.
    C. annually.
    D. every three years.

_____ 30. Which of the following is a site preparation requirement for service testing fire hose? (681)

    A. Area with no grade to it

    B. Completely gated or fenced

    C. Smooth and free from rocks and debris

    D. Building structures to simulate occupancies

_____ 31. Which of the following are needed when service testing fire hose? (681)

    A. Salvage covers

    B. Camera or video recorders

    C. Nozzles with shutoff valves

    D. Extension or combination ladders

_____ 32. Which of the following is a valve with a 1/4-inch (6 mm) hole in the gate that permits pressurizing the hose but does not allow water to surge through the hose if it fails? (681)

    A. Hose test gate valve

    B. Hose test ball valve

    C. Hose test shutoff valve

    D. Hose test butterfly valve

_____ 33. Test lengths of hose should not exceed: (682)

    A. 300 feet (100 m) in length.

    B. 400 feet (120 m) in length.

    C. 500 feet (150 m) in length.

    D. 600 feet (180 m) in length.

_____ 34. When service testing fire hose, close all valves _____ to prevent water hammer in the hose and pump. (682)

    A. slowly

    B. quickly

    C. partially

    D. forcefully

_____ 1. Which of the following is a process or evolution that changes a liquid into a gaseous state? (718)
   A. Dilution
   B. Dissipation
   C. Adsorption
   D. Vaporization

_____ 2. Which of the following refers to the amount of heat energy required to raise the temperature of a specified mass of a substance by one degree? (718)
   A. Specific Heat
   B. Vaporization Point
   C. Point of Expansion
   D. Latent Heat of Vaporization

_____ 3. Which of the following refers to the quantity of heat absorbed by a substance at the point at which it changes from a liquid to a vapor? (718)
   A. Specific Heat
   B. Vaporization Point
   C. Point of Expansion
   D. Latent Heat of Vaporization

_____ 4. At 212°F (100°C), water expands approximately _____ times its original volume when converted to steam. (720)
   A. 200
   B. 900
   C. 1,700
   D. 2,300

_____ 5. When water is converted to steam rather than simply heated to its boiling point, it absorbs: (720)
   A. much less heat.
   B. much more heat.
   C. no heat at all.
   D. the same amount of heat.

6. Which of the following statements about water as an extinguishing agent is MOST accurate? (722)

A. Water has a greater heat-absorbing capacity than most common extinguishing agents.

B. Water has a lesser heat-absorbing capacity than most common extinguishing agents.

C. Water has the same heat-absorbing capacity as most common extinguishing agents.

D. Water is not the first choice as an extinguishing agent because of its lack of heat-absorbing capacity.

7. Which of the following terms refers to that part of total pressure that is lost while forcing water through pipes, fittings, fire hose, and adapters? (722)

A. Friction loss

B. Operating loss

C. Vibration loss

D. Movement loss

8. In general, the smaller the hose diameter and the longer the hose lay: (723)

A. the higher the friction loss at a given pressure and flow volume.

B. the lower the friction loss at a given pressure and flow volume.

C. the less affected the hose is by pressure and flow volume changes.

D. are factors that do not substantially affect friction loss in any way.

9. Which of the following is NOT generally a reason for increased friction loss? (723)

A. Rough linings in fire hose

B. More adapters than necessary

C. Hoselines longer than necessary

D. Hoseline that has not been "broken in"

10. When a nozzle is above the fire pump, there is a: (723)

A. pressure loss.

B. pressure gain.

C. friction loss.

D. friction gain.

11. When a nozzle is below the pump, there is a: (723)

A. pressure loss.

B. pressure gain.

C. friction loss.

D. friction gain.

12. To prevent water hammer when water is flowing, nozzles, hydrants, valves, and hose clamps should generally be: (724)
    A. closed quickly.
    B. closed slowly.
    C. closed partially.
    D. closed forcefully.

13. Which of the following fire streams discharges less than 40 gpm (160 L/min) including those fed by booster lines? (724)
    A. Handline stream
    B. Master stream
    C. Low-volume stream
    D. Mid-volume stream

14. Which of the following fire streams is supplied by 1½- to 3-inch (38 mm to 77 mm) hose, with flows from 40 to 350 gpm (160 L/min to 1 400 L/min)? (724)
    A. Handline stream
    B. Master stream
    C. Low-volume stream
    D. Mid-volume stream

15. Which of the following fire streams discharges more than 350 gpm (1 400 L/min)? (725)
    A. Handline stream
    B. Master stream
    C. Low-volume stream
    D. Mid-volume stream

16. The volume of water discharged is determined by the design of the nozzle and the: (725)
    A. expertise of the nozzle operator.
    B. water pressure at the nozzle.
    C. water pressure at the pump.
    D. outside temperature and wind.

17. Which of the following fire streams is compact with little shower or spray and has the ability to reach areas that other streams might not reach? (726)
    A. Fog stream
    B. Solid stream
    C. Broken stream
    D. Compacted stream

Firefighter I

_____ 18. Which of the following statements about solid streams is MOST accurate? (727)

    A. They are more prone to clogging with debris.

    B. They cannot be used to apply compressed-air foam.

    C. They have greater penetration power than other types of streams.

    D. They are more likely to disturb normal thermal layering than other types of streams.

_____ 19. Which of the following is a disadvantage of solid streams? (728)

    A. Produce less steam conversion than fog nozzles

    B. Hoselines more easily kinked at corners and obstructions

    C. May be easier to maneuver due to lower operating pressures

    D. Operate at reduced nozzle pressures per gallon (liter) than other types of streams

_____ 20. Which of the following fire streams is a fine spray composed of tiny water droplets? (728)

    A. Fog stream

    B. Solid stream

    C. Broken stream

    D. Compacted stream

_____ 21. Which of the following nozzles allow the nozzle operator to vary the flow rate while maintaining a consistent nozzle pressure? (730)

    A. Standard nozzles

    B. Automatic nozzles

    C. Self-adjusting nozzles

    D. Manually adjustable nozzles

_____ 22. The rate of discharge from a manually adjustable fog nozzle can be changed by: (730)

    A. entering in the desired gpm (L/min) setting.

    B. rotating the selector ring to a specific gpm (L/min) setting.

    C. pushing the selector button up or down to a specific gpm (L/min) setting.

    D. moving the selector clamp up or down to a specific gpm (L/min) setting.

_____ 23. The designed operating pressure for most combination nozzles is: (731)

    A. 45 psi (315 kPa).

    B. 50 psi (350 kPa).

    C. 75 psi (525 kPa).

    D. 100 psi (700 kPa).

Firefighter I

24. Which of the following streams is MOST likely to be able to provide protection to firefighters? (731)
    A. Solid stream
    B. Broken stream
    C. Wide-angle fog pattern
    D. Narrow-angle fog pattern

25. Which of the following is a disadvantage of fog streams? (731)
    A. Fog streams increase heat.
    B. Fog streams cannot be used to aid ventilation.
    C. The discharge pattern of fog streams cannot be adjusted.
    D. Fog streams may disturb thermal layering if applied incorrectly.

26. A cellar nozzle is an example of a: (731)
    A. fog nozzle.
    B. broken stream nozzle.
    C. combination nozzle.
    D. solid stream nozzle.

27. On which of the following types of fires are broken stream nozzles MOST effective? (731)
    A. Electrical fires
    B. Wildland fires
    C. Flammable liquid fires
    D. Fires in confined spaces such as attics

28. On which of the following classes of fires are broken stream nozzles LEAST effective? (731)
    A. Class A
    B. Class B
    C. Class C
    D. Class D

29. When handling solid-stream nozzles, increasing the nozzle discharge pressure and flow rate: (732)
    A. increases nozzle reaction.
    B. decreases nozzle reaction.
    C. has no affect on nozzle reaction.
    D. may either increase or decrease nozzle reaction.

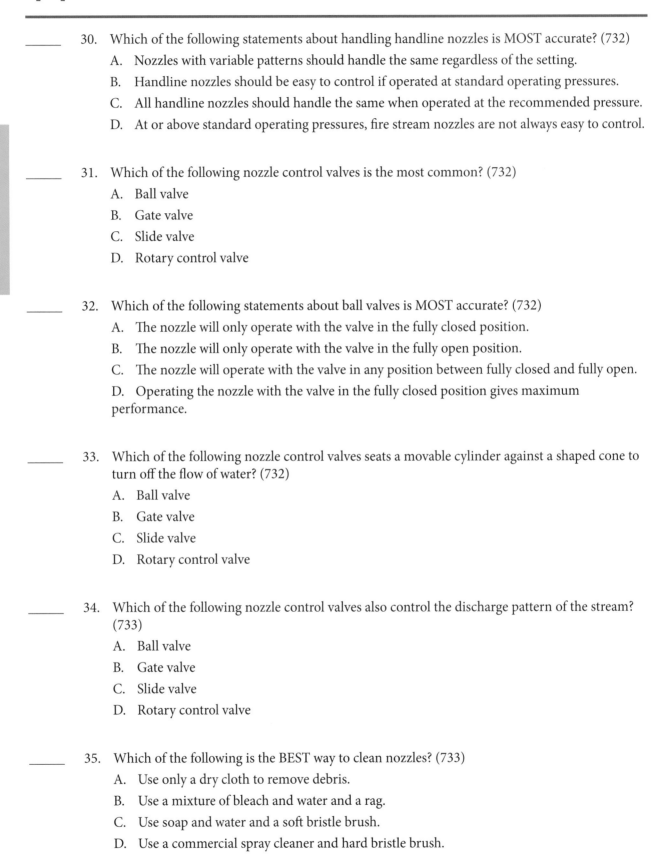

_____ 30. Which of the following statements about handling handline nozzles is MOST accurate? (732)

    A. Nozzles with variable patterns should handle the same regardless of the setting.

    B. Handline nozzles should be easy to control if operated at standard operating pressures.

    C. All handline nozzles should handle the same when operated at the recommended pressure.

    D. At or above standard operating pressures, fire stream nozzles are not always easy to control.

_____ 31. Which of the following nozzle control valves is the most common? (732)

    A. Ball valve

    B. Gate valve

    C. Slide valve

    D. Rotary control valve

_____ 32. Which of the following statements about ball valves is MOST accurate? (732)

    A. The nozzle will only operate with the valve in the fully closed position.

    B. The nozzle will only operate with the valve in the fully open position.

    C. The nozzle will operate with the valve in any position between fully closed and fully open.

    D. Operating the nozzle with the valve in the fully closed position gives maximum performance.

_____ 33. Which of the following nozzle control valves seats a movable cylinder against a shaped cone to turn off the flow of water? (732)

    A. Ball valve

    B. Gate valve

    C. Slide valve

    D. Rotary control valve

_____ 34. Which of the following nozzle control valves also control the discharge pattern of the stream? (733)

    A. Ball valve

    B. Gate valve

    C. Slide valve

    D. Rotary control valve

_____ 35. Which of the following is the BEST way to clean nozzles? (733)

    A. Use only a dry cloth to remove debris.

    B. Use a mixture of bleach and water and a rag.

    C. Use soap and water and a soft bristle brush.

    D. Use a commercial spray cleaner and hard bristle brush.

Firefighter II

_____ 1. Which of the following ways of extinguishing and/or preventing fire when using fire fighting foam creates a barrier between the fuel and the fire? (734)

A. Cooling

B. Separating

C. Smothering

D. Penetrating

_____ 2. Which of the following ways of extinguishing and/or preventing fire when using fire fighting foam lowers the temperature of the fuel and adjacent surfaces? (734)

A. Cooling

B. Separating

C. Smothering

D. Penetrating

_____ 3. Which of the following ways of extinguishing and/or preventing fire when using fire fighting foam lowers the surface tension of water and allows it to penetrate deep-seated fires? (734)

A. Cooling

B. Separating

C. Smothering

D. Penetrating

_____ 4. Which of the following ways of extinguishing and/or preventing fire suppresses the release of flammable vapors and therefore reduces the possibility of ignition or reignition? (734)

A. Cooling

B. Separating

C. Smothering

D. Penetrating

_____ 5. Which of the following refers to fuels which are petroleum-based combustible or flammable liquids that float on water? (734)

A. Polar solvents

B. Natural fuels

C. Synthetic fuels

D. Hydrocarbon fuels

_____ 6. Which of the following refers to flammable liquids that mix readily with water? (735)
   A. Polar solvents
   B. Natural fuels
   C. Synthetic fuels
   D. Hydrocarbon fuels

_____ 7. Which of the following terms refers to raw foam liquid before the introduction of water and air? (735)
   A. Batch foam
   B. Finished foam
   C. Foam solution
   D. Foam concentrate

_____ 8. Which of the following terms refers to a mixture of foam concentrate and water before the introduction of air? (735)
   A. Foam base
   B. Batch foam
   C. Finished foam
   D. Foam solution

_____ 9. Which of the following terms refers to the completed product after air is introduced into the foam solution? (735)
   A. Batch foam
   B. Foam mixture
   C. Finished foam
   D. Foam concentrate

_____ 10. Which of the following is a device that introduces foam concentrate into the water stream to make foam solution? (735)
   A. Foam mixer
   B. Foam hydrator
   C. Foam developer
   D. Foam proportioner

_____ 11. Which of the following is NOT an element needed to produce fire fighting foam? (735)
   A. Air
   B. Water
   C. Carbon dioxide
   D. Foam concentrate

_____ 12. Which of the following is needed to produce an adequate amount of foam bubbles to form an effective foam blanket? (735)

 A. Aeration
 B. Nitrogen
 C. Carbon dioxide
 D. Temperature variation

_____ 13. Which of the following foams is most commonly used at the rate of from 20:1 to 200:1 through hydraulically operated nozzle-style delivery devices? (736)

 A. Low-expansion foam
 B. Medium-expansion foam
 C. High-expansion foam
 D. Super-expansion foam

_____ 14. Which of the following foams is basically a wetting agent that reduces the surface tension of water and allows it to soak into combustible materials easier than plain water? (736)

 A. Class A foam
 B. Class B foam
 C. Class C foam
 D. All-purpose foam

_____ 15. Which of the following foams is used to prevent the ignition of or to extinguish fires involving flammable and combustible liquids? (736)

 A. Class A foam
 B. Class B foam
 C. Class C foam
 D. All-purpose foam

_____ 16. When using Class B foams on unignited spills, how thick should the blanket of foam be that is applied to the fuel surface? (737)

 A. 2 inches (50 mm)
 B. 4 inches (100 mm)
 C. 8 inches (200 mm)
 D. 10 inches (250 mm)

_____ 17. Most fire fighting foam concentrates are intended to be mixed with: (738)

 A. 40 to 55 percent water.
 B. 55 to 74 percent water.
 C. 74 to 99.9 percent water.
 D. 94 to 99.9 percent water.

Firefighter II

Firefighter II

_____ 18. Which of the following methods of proportioning foam uses the pressure energy in the stream of water to draft foam concentrate into the fire stream? (740)

A. Injection

B. Induction

C. Premixing

D. Batch-mixing

_____ 19. Which of the following methods of proportioning foam uses an external pump or head pressure to force foam concentrate into the fire stream at the correct ratio for the water flow? (740)

A. Injection

B. Induction

C. Premixing

D. Batch-mixing

_____ 20. Which of the following methods of proportioning foam is the simplest and most accurate method of mixing foam concentrate and water? (740)

A. Injection

B. Induction

C. Premixing

D. Batch-mixing

_____ 21. Which of the following is a drawback of batch-mixing? (740-741)

A. Batch-mixing is not effective for smaller incidents.

B. Batch-mixing is complicated and requires precise measurements.

C. Batch-mixing cannot be used with certain foams such as Class A foams.

D. All water tanks in which foam was batch-mixed must be thoroughly flushed with plain water.

_____ 22. Which of the following methods of proportioning foam is typically used with portable extinguishers, wheeled extinguishers, skid-mounted twin-agent units, and vehicle-mounted tank systems? (741)

A. Injection

B. Induction

C. Premixing

D. Batch-mixing

_____ 23. Which of the following foam proportioners is the most common type of foam proportioner used in the fire service? (742)

A. Foam nozzle eductor

B. In-line foam eductor

C. Balanced-pressure proportioner

D. Compressed-air foam system (CAFS)

_____ 24. Which of the following foam proportioners is designed to be directly attached to the pump panel discharge outlet or connected at some point in the hose lay? (742)
- A. Foam nozzle eductor
- B. In-line foam eductor
- C. Balanced-pressure proportioner
- D. Compressed-air foam system (CAFS)

_____ 25. Which of the following foam proportioners uses the Venturi Principle to draft foam concentrate into the water stream? (742)
- A. Foam nozzle injector
- B. In-line foam eductor
- C. Balanced-pressure proportioner
- D. Compressed-air foam system (CAFS)

_____ 26. Which of the following foam proportioners is built into the nozzle rather than into the hoseline? (742)
- A. Foam nozzle eductor
- B. In-line foam eductor
- C. Balanced-pressure proportioner
- D. Compressed-air foam system (CAFS)

_____ 27. In which of the following foam proportioners does the hoseline contain the finished foam? (743-744)
- A. Foam nozzle eductor
- B. In-line foam eductor
- C. Balanced-pressure proportioner
- D. Compressed-air foam system (CAFS)

_____ 28. Which of the following is a disadvantage of using compressed-air foam? (744)
- A. Hose reaction can be significant.
- B. Foam produced is not very durable.
- C. Stream reach is shorter than with other foam systems.
- D. Hoselines are heavier than those full of water or foam solution.

_____ 29. Solid-bore nozzles are most often used with: (744)
- A. foam nozzle eductors.
- B. in-line foam eductors.
- C. balanced-pressure proportioners.
- D. compressed-air foam systems (CAFS).

Firefighter II

_____ 30. Which of the following handline nozzles is the most effective appliance for the generation of low-expansion foam? (745)

A. Fog nozzle

B. Solid-bore nozzle

C. Air-aspirating foam nozzle

D. Water-aspirating type nozzle

_____ 31. Which of the following handline nozzles can be used with foam solutions to produce a low-expansion, short-lasting foam and works best when used with regular AFFF and class A foams? (745)

A. Fog nozzle

B. Solid-bore nozzle

C. Air-aspirating foam nozzle

D. Water-aspirating type nozzle

_____ 32. Which of the following statements about fog nozzles is MOST accurate? (745)

A. Fog nozzles can be used on polar solvent fires.

B. These nozzles can be used with protein and fluoroprotein foams.

C. The best application of fog nozzles is when used with AFFF and Class A foams.

D. These nozzles cannot be used with alcohol-resistant AFFF foams on hydrocarbon fires.

_____ 33. Which of the following foam generators produces a foam with a high air content and is typically associated with total-flooding applications? (746)

A. Air-aspirating foam nozzle

B. Electrical blower generator

C. Water-aspirating type nozzle

D. Mechanical blower generator

_____ 34. Which of the following is a reason for failure to generate foam or for generating poor-quality foam? (746)

A. Nozzle is fully open

B. Nozzle is too far above the eductor

C. Eductor and nozzle flow ratings match

D. Only one type of foam concentrate is used

_____ 35. Which of the following foam application techniques directs the foam stream on the ground near the front edge of a burning liquid spill? (747)

A. Roll-on method

B. Bank-down method

C. Rain-down method

D. Combination method

36. Which of the following foam application techniques directs the foam stream onto an elevated object near or within the area of a burning pool of liquid or an unignited liquid spill? (747)
    A. Roll-on method
    B. Bank-down method
    C. Rain-down method
    D. Combination method

37. Which of the following foam application techniques directs the stream into the air above the fire or spill and allows the foam to float gently down onto the surface of the fuel? (747-748)
    A. Roll-on method
    B. Bank-down method
    C. Rain-down method
    D. Combination method

38. What should be consulted for information on any specific foam concentrate? (749)
    A. Incident reports
    B. Product sales receipt
    C. Departmental SOPs
    D. Material safety data sheets (MSDS)

39. In the United States, Class A foams should be approved for environmental suitability by the: (749)
    A. USDA Forest Service.
    B. United States Fire Administration.
    C. National Institute for Occupational Safety.
    D. Occupational Health and Safety Administration.

40. Foam concentrates, either at full strengths or in diluted forms: (749)
    A. pose no health risks to firefighters.
    B. may be mildly irritating to the skin and eyes.
    C. may be extremely irritating to the skin and eyes.
    D. may cause a variety of serious health problems.

41. The biodegradability of a foam is determined by the: (749)
    A. rate at which it dissipates into the air.
    B. rate at which it soaks into the ground.
    C. rate at which it is able to extinguish the fire.
    D. rate at which environmental bacteria cause it to decompose.

_____ 42. Which of the following is the MOST likely environmental damage from foam? (749)
  A. Killing of birds that fly above the area in which foam was applied
  B. Killing of trees and shrubbery near where the foam was applied
  C. Killing of mammals near the area where the foam was applied
  D. Killing of fish and other aquatic creatures in waterways near where foam was applied

Firefighter II

_____ 1. Which of the following fire department personnel decides if the fire attack is to be conducted as an offensive or defensive operation? (762)

A. Fire Chief

B. Safety Officer

C. Incident Commander

D. Public Information Officer

_____ 2. If a door to the fire area must be opened while making entry, all members of the hose team should stay: (766)

A. centered in the doorway.

B. low and to one side of the doorway.

C. standing and to one side of the doorway.

D. low and split on either side of the doorway.

_____ 3. If a door is very hot, which of the following will happen when checking for heat prior to opening it? (766)

A. Water applied to the door will cause the door to fail.

B. Water applied to the door will pool at the base of the door.

C. Water applied to the door will damage the surface of the door.

D. Water applied to the door will evaporate and convert to steam.

_____ 4. A fire that cannot be seen from a doorway because objects are obstructing it is called a(n): (767)

A. attack fire.

B. blocked fire.

C. shielded fire.

D. effective fire.

_____ 5. Water applied to a fire in short bursts directly onto the burning fuels is often called: (767)

A. painting.

B. penning.

C. penciling.

D. partitioning.

_____ 6. Which of the following types of attack involves the discharge of water or a foam stream straight onto the burning fuel? (767)

    A. Lead attack

    B. Direct attack

    C. Indirect attack

    D. Combination attack

_____ 7. Which of the following types of attack involves directing fire streams toward the ceiling of a room or building in order to generate a large amount of steam? (768)

    A. Lead attack

    B. Direct attack

    C. Indirect attack

    D. Combination attack

_____ 8. Which of the following types of attack pairs the steam-generating technique of a ceiling-level attack with an attack on the burning materials near floor level? (768)

    A. Multi-attack

    B. Direct attack

    C. Indirect attack

    D. Combination attack

_____ 9. Which of the following is NOT one of the three main uses for a master stream? (769)

    A. Direct fire attack

    B. Backup handlines

    C. Indirect fire attack

    D. Exposure protection

_____ 10. A large-caliber water stream usually supplied by siamesing two or more hoselines into a manifold device that delivers 350 gpm (1 400 L/min) or more is a: (769)

    A. fog stream.

    B. low stream.

    C. high stream.

    D. master stream.

_____ 11. Which of the following statements about deploying master stream devices is MOST accurate? (769)

    A. Firefighters should aim the stream so it enters the structure at an upward angle.

    B. Moving a master stream device can be conducted while the device is in operation.

    C. When a master stream device is directed into a building, it must be positioned far away from the building.

    D. Streams that enter an opening at a low or horizontal angle are extremely effective and enable firefighters to maintain control.

_____ 12. Once a portable master stream device is in place, how many firefighters are required to operate it? (770)

A. 1

B. 2

C. 3

D. 4

_____ 13. Apparatus equipped with hydraulically operated ladders or booms and used to deliver elevated master streams are called: (771)

A. boom devices.

B. aerial devices.

C. hydraulic stream lifts.

D. master stream elevators.

_____ 14. Which of the following definitions best describes a quint? (771)

A. An aerial ladder with an attached platform

B. A pumper equipped with a hydraulically operated extension ladder

C. A rotating, power-operated ladder mounted on a self-propelled fire apparatus

D. An engine equipped with hydraulically operated booms dedicated to applying water

_____ 15. Which of the following definitions best describes an aerial ladder? (771)

A. A ladder with an attached platform

B. A pumper equipped with a hydraulically operated extension

C. A rotating, power-operated ladder mounted on a self-propelled fire apparatus

D. An engine equipped with hydraulically operated booms dedicated to applying water

_____ 16. A power-operated aerial device that combines an aerial ladder with a personnel-carrying platform supported at the end of the ladder is known as a(n): (772)

A. aerial ladder platform.

B. mobile platform ladder.

C. supported aerial system.

D. articulating aerial platform.

_____ 17. An aerial device in which the supporting structural member is hinged and operates in a folding manner is known as a(n): (772)

A. aerial ladder platform.

B. mobile platform ladder.

C. supported aerial system.

D. articulating aerial platform.

18. What is a water tower? (772)

   A. A ladder with an attached platform

   B. A pumper equipped with an extension ladder

   C. A rotating, power-operated ladder mounted on a self-propelled fire apparatus

   D. An engine equipped with hydraulically operated booms dedicated to applying water

19. Once the electrical power to Class C fires is turned off, they may self-extinguish or: (780)

   A. explode.

   B. re-energize.

   C. fall into Class A or B fires if they continue to burn.

   D. fall into Class D fires if they continue to burn.

20. When should electrical power to an entire building be shut off during a Class C fire? (781)

   A. When ordered

   B. Upon arrival at the scene

   C. When the fire is reported

   D. Upon termination of the fire

21. A toxic compound which firefighters must be aware of that can be found in some older oil-filled electric transformers is known as: (782)

   A. asbestos.

   B. methane.

   C. chlorofluorocarbon.

   D. polychlorinated biphenyl.

22. Which of the following statements about commercial high-voltage installations is MOST accurate? (782-783)

   A. Entry personnel should wear a tag line.

   B. Entry personnel do not have to wear SCBA.

   C. Firefighters should enter these installations for extinguishment purposes only.

   D. Water, in the form of fog, should be used in extinguishing fires in commercial high-voltage installations.

23. With whom should firefighters verify that electrical and gas utilities have been shut off before cutting into walls that may contain electrical wiring and gas piping? (783)

   A. Safety Officer

   B. Building engineer

   C. Incident Commander

   D. Utility company personnel

Firefighter I

24. Which of the following statements regarding controlling electrical power is MOST accurate? (783)
    A. Power should be shut off to the entire building.
    B. Turning off the master switch turns off the power entirely.
    C. It is often advantageous for electrical power to remain on to provide lighting.
    D. Removing the electric meter guarantees that the flow of electricity will be stopped.

25. Which of the following is NOT one of the factors most affecting the seriousness of electrical shock? (785)
    A. Elasticity of skin
    B. Available current
    C. Length of exposure
    D. Degree of skin resistance

26. Firefighters should use fog streams with at least how much nozzle pressure on energized electrical equipment? (785)
    A. 70 psi (490 kPa)
    B. 80 psi (560 kPa)
    C. 90 psi (630 kPa)
    D. 100 psi (700 kPa)

27. Which of the following statements about suppressing Class D fires is MOST accurate? (787)
    A. Class D fires burn at low temperatures.
    B. Class D fires are not reactive to water.
    C. Combustible metal fires can be recognized by a brilliant white light.
    D. Combustible metal fires cool extremely quickly after they appear to be out.

28. Which of the following Class D materials is MOST reactive to water? (787)
    A. Large castings
    B. Small wood chips
    C. Small metal chips
    D. Finished metal products

29. Which of the following is the highest priority for the first engine company? (789)
    A. Protect rescuers.
    B. Assist in extinguishment.
    C. Protect secondary means of egress.
    D. Protect the most threatened exposure.

Firefighter I

_____ 30. Backing up the initial attack line is a priority of the: (789)

    A. first engine company.

    B. Rapid Intervention Crew.

    C. second engine company.

    D. fireground support company.

_____ 31. Ladder placement is a priority of the: (790)

    A. first engine company.

    B. Rapid Intervention Crew.

    C. second engine company.

    D. fireground support company.

_____ 32. What is a blitz attack? (790)

    A. To aggressively attack a fire from the exterior with a large diameter fire stream

    B. To aggressively attack a fire from the interior with a large diameter fire stream

    C. To offensively attack a fire from the exterior with a small diameter fire stream

    D. To offensively attack a fire from the interior with a small diameter fire stream

_____ 33. Two or more fully equipped and immediately available firefighters designated to stand by outside the hazard zone to enter and rescue firefighters inside is known as a(n): (791-792)

    A. first engine company.

    B. Rapid Intervention Crew.

    C. second engine company.

    D. fireground support company.

_____ 34. Where is the fire attack typically initiated in fires in upper levels of structures? (793)

    A. From the floor above the fire floor

    B. From the floor below the fire floor

    C. From two floors above the fire floor

    D. From two floors below the fire floor

_____ 35. Where is the staging of extra equipment and personnel usually established in fires in upper levels of structures? (793)

    A. The floor above the fire floor

    B. The floor below the fire floor

    C. Two floors above the fire floor

    D. Two floors below the fire floor

36. Which of the following statements about fires belowground in structures is MOST accurate? (793)

    A. It is always impossible to control the fire without entering the basement.

    B. After a few minutes of operation of a cellar nozzle, an increase in heat should be detectible.

    C. While entering the basement, the fire attack team should descend the stairs behind the protection of a wide-angle fog pattern.

    D. If firefighters must enter the basement, a ventilation opening should be made at the end of the basement adjacent to the entry stairway.

37. Unprotected steel girders and other supports elongate when exposed to temperatures of: (795)

    A. 700°F (371°C) or more.

    B. 800°F (427°C) or more.

    C. 900°F (482°C) or more.

    D. 1,000°F (538°C) or more.

38. Which of the following is a danger involved when dealing with fires in occupancies with fixed fire extinguishing systems? (795)

    A. Toxic environments

    B. Carbon monoxide depletion

    C. De-energized electrical equipment

    D. Lack of personnel to close OS&Y valve

39. Attack line for a vehicle fire should be at LEAST: (796)

    A. ½-inch (13 mm) hoseline.

    B. ¾-inch (20 mm) hoseline.

    C. 1-inch (25 mm) hoseline.

    D. 1½-inch (38 mm) hoseline.

40. From which of the following positions should a vehicle fire be attacked, when possible? (796)

    A. From the side and from upwind and uphill

    B. From the front and from upwind and uphill

    C. From the side and from downwind and downhill

    D. From the front and from downwind and downhill

41. Which of the following statements regarding basic procedures at vehicle fires is MOST accurate? (797-798)

    A. Extinguish fire near vehicle occupants last.

    B. Attack the fire from a 90-degree angle to the long axis of the vehicle.

    C. One of the first actions firefighters should take is to establish a safe working zone.

    D. In many engine compartment fires, the hood must be opened before the fire can be controlled.

_____ 42. Which of the following is one of the three methods recommended for use for fires in the undercarriage of a vehicle? (798)

    A. Leave the hood closed and direct the stream through the cracks.

    B. Open the hood and direct the stream through the engine compartment.

    C. If the vehicle is on a hard surface such as concrete or asphalt, direct the stream upward toward the vehicle.

    D. If there is a hazard in getting close to the vehicle, use a fog stream from a distance to reach under the vehicle.

_____ 43. Which of the following colors of electrical cables should not be cut in hybrid vehicles due to the fact that they are high-voltage systems? (799)

    A. Red

    B. Blue

    C. Orange

    D. Yellow

_____ 44. Which of the following statements about trash container fires is MOST accurate? (799)

    A. Fires in small piles of trash require master streams.

    B. Larger piles of trash are often extinguished with booster line.

    C. Class C foam is recommended for extinguishment of most trash container fires.

    D. Once the fire has been controlled, standard overhaul techniques may be used.

_____ 45. Which of the following is the minimum amount of protection that should be worn at a trash container fire? (799)

    A. Full PPE with SCBA

    B. Station/work uniforms

    C. Full PPE without SCBA

    D. Wildland personal protective clothing

_____ 46. Which of the following statements regarding fires in confined spaces is MOST accurate? (800)

    A. Fires in confined spaces should always be attacked directly.

    B. The command post and staging area must be established inside the hot zone.

    C. An attendant must be stationed at the confined space entrance to track personnel and equipment entering and leaving the space.

    D. The single most important factor in safely operating at emergencies in confined spaces is recognizing the properties of the fuel.

_____ 47. Which of the following is one of the three main influences on wildland fire behavior? (800-801)

    A. Weather

    B. Personnel

    C. Extinguishing agent

    D. Proximity to urban areas

48. Roots are classified as which of the following types of fuel? (801-802)
    A. Aerial fuel
    B. Surface fuel
    C. Subsurface fuel
    D. Anti-surface fuel

49. Downed limbs are classified as which of the following types of fuel? (801-802)
    A. Aerial fuel
    B. Surface fuel
    C. Subsurface fuel
    D. Anti-surface fuel

50. To be classified as an aerial fuel, brush must be at least: (802)
    A. 3 feet (1 m) tall.
    B. 4 feet (1.3 m) tall.
    C. 5 feet (1.6 m) tall.
    D. 6 feet (2 m) tall.

51. Which of the following is a factor that affects the burning characteristics of fuels? (802)
    A. Light fuels burn slower than heavier ones.
    B. When fuels are close together, the fire spreads slower.
    C. Tightly compacted fuels, such as hay bales, burn faster than those that are loosely piled.
    D. As fuels dry out, they burn with greater intensity than those with higher moisture content.

52. The physical configuration of the land or terrain is the: (803)
    A. crust.
    B. topography.
    C. mountainous region.
    D. subcutaneous earth.

53. The compass direction a slope faces is its: (803)
    A. aspect.
    B. degree.
    C. location.
    D. component.

_____ 54. The narrow V-shaped ravine in which wind movement can be critical in wildland fires is known as a: (803)

A. chute.

B. gulley.

C. saddle.

D. valley.

_____ 55. The area where the fire started is the: (803)

A. head.

B. origin.

C. finger.

D. perimeter.

_____ 56. Which of the following is the part of a wildland fire that spreads most rapidly? (803)

A. Head

B. Flank

C. Green

D. Island

_____ 57. Long narrow strips of fire extending from the main fire are known as: (803)

A. lengths.

B. striping.

C. fingers.

D. arrows.

_____ 58. Which of the following terms is known as the rear of the wildland fire? (804)

A. Head

B. Heel

C. Black

D. Green

_____ 59. What is the green? (804)

A. The sides of a wildland fire

B. The outer boundary of the fire

C. The area in which the fire has consumed the fuels

D. The area of unburned fuels next to the involved area

_____ 60. What is the black? (804)
  A. The sides of a wildland fire
  B. The outer boundary of the fire
  C. The area in which the fire has consumed the fuels
  D. The area of unburned fuels next to the involved area

_____ 61. Which of the following statements about wildland protective clothing and equipment is MOST accurate? (805)
  A. Eye protection is optional.
  B. One-piece jumpsuits are dangerous.
  C. Most wildland fire agencies provide firefighters with a canteen and backpack.
  D. NFPA® 1001 specifies minimum PPE for firefighters to participate in wildland fire fighting.

_____ 62. Action taken straight against the flames at a wildland fire's edge is: (805)
  A. direct attack.
  B. indirect attack.
  C. concentrated attack.
  D. noncontained attack.

_____ 63. The attack used at varying distances from the advancing wildland fire is: (805)
  A. direct attack.
  B. indirect attack.
  C. concentrated attack.
  D. noncontained attack.

_____ 64. Which of the following is NOT one of the Ten Standard Fire Fighting Orders? (806)
  A. Post lookouts at all times.
  B. Know what the fire is doing at all times.
  C. Keep informed on fire weather conditions and forecasts.
  D. Base all actions on current and expected behavior of the fire.

Fire Control

_____ 1. Which of the following is the agent most often used to extinguish structure fires? (763-764)
   A. Foam
   B. Water
   C. Powders
   D. Chemicals

_____ 2. Non-collapsible rubber-covered, rubber-lined hose usually wound on a reel, mounted on an engine, and used for initial attack on incipient or smoldering fires is known as: (764)
   A. initial hose.
   B. master hose.
   C. support hose.
   D. booster hose.

_____ 3. Which of the following is NOT a factor in hoseline selection? (764)
   A. Stream reach needed
   B. Fire load and material involved
   C. Need for speed and mobility
   D. Whether or not a pre-incident plan exists

_____ 4. Which of the following is the SMALLEST handline size that should be used for interior fire fighting? (764)
   A. ¾-inch (20 mm)
   B. 1-inch (25 mm)
   C. 1½-inch (38 mm)
   D. 1¾-inch (45 mm)

_____ 5. Which of the following nozzles can project water in a range of patterns? (764)
   A. Master nozzle
   B. Pattern nozzle
   C. Solid-stream nozzle
   D. Combination nozzle

_____ 6. Which of the following types of streams provides the greatest reach? (764)
   A. Broken stream
   B. Straight stream
   C. Wide-angle fog stream
   D. Narrow-angle fog stream

_____ 7. Which of the following types of streams can protect firefighters from radiant heat but can also be easily affected by wind? (764)

A. Solid stream

B. Broken stream

C. Straight stream

D. Wide-angle fog stream

_____ 8. Which of the following is critical in heat absorption? (764)

A. Stream angle

B. Stream temperature

C. Converting water to steam

D. Converting steam to water

_____ 9. Which of the following is an example of a Class B fire? (773)

A. Paper fire

B. Alcohol fire

C. Electrical fire

D. Magnesium fire

_____ 10. Flammable liquids are those that have flash points of: (773)

A. less than 100°F (38°C).

B. less than 200°F (93°C).

C. higher than 100°F (38°C).

D. higher than 200°F (93°C).

_____ 11. Combustible liquids are those that have flash points of: (773)

A. less than 100°F (38°C).

B. less than 200°F (93°C).

C. higher than 100°F (38°C).

D. higher than 200°F (93°C).

_____ 12. What is the FIRST precaution firefighters must exercise when attacking large fires involving flammable and combustible liquids? (773)

A. Stop the leak.

B. Wear station uniforms.

C. Control all ignition sources in the area.

D. Avoid standing in pools of fuel or runoff water.

_____ 13. The rapid vaporization of a liquid stored under pressure upon release to the atmosphere following major failure of its containing vessel is: (774)

    A. pressurized vapor failure.

    B. atmospheric liquid vaporization.

    C. rapid liquidized pressure release.

    D. boiling liquid expanding vapor explosion.

_____ 14. Which of the following agents is most often used to control flammable liquid fires? (774)

    A. Foam

    B. Water

    C. Powder

    D. Dry chemical

_____ 15. Which of the following substances DOES NOT mix with water? (775)

    A. Lacquer

    B. Alcohol

    C. Ammonia

    D. Petroleum

_____ 16. Which of the following substances DOES mix with water? (775)

    A. Gasoline

    B. Kerosene

    C. Alcohol

    D. Petroleum

_____ 17. What is MOST useful as a cooling agent for protecting exposures? (775)

    A. Foam

    B. Water

    C. Powders

    D. Chemicals

_____ 18. Which of the following statements regarding the use of mechanical tools to control Class B fires with water is MOST accurate? (775-776)

    A. Class B fuels should be flushed into sewers.

    B. Water is not recommended for dissipating flammable vapors.

    C. Water can be used to move Class B fuels to areas where they can safely burn.

    D. Plunging a stream into burning flammable liquids greatly decreases fire intensity.

Firefighter II

_____ 19. Which of the following statements regarding crew protection while using water to control Class B fires is MOST accurate? (776)

    A. Cooling tanks supports causes their collapse.

    B. Faster movements provide the most safety from flames and heat.

    C. Approach horizontal pressure vessels that are involved in fire at a right angle to the side.

    D. Hose teams can be advanced under wide protective fog patterns to make temporary repairs.

_____ 20. When controlling Class B fires, approaches to the storage vessels exposed to the fire should be made at: (776)

    A. 30-degree angles to the tanks.

    B. 45-degree angles to the tanks.

    C. 60-degree angles to the tanks.

    D. 75-degree angles to the tanks.

_____ 21. Which of the following is a major difference in fires in vehicles transporting flammable fuels and in flammable liquid storage facilities? (777)

    A. Increased water supply

    B. Ease in containing spills

    C. Decreased life-safety risks to motorists

    D. Damaged tanks caused by the force of collisions

_____ 22. Which of the following statements about bulk transport vehicle fires is MOST accurate? (777-778)

    A. Road flares should be used to alert oncoming motorists.

    B. Most incidents require the stopping or re-routing of traffic.

    C. Techniques for extinguishment are very different from fires in flammable fuel storage facilities.

    D. Techniques of approaching and controlling fires involving vehicles are the same as for storage vessels.

_____ 23. How many lanes of traffic in addition to the incident lane should be closed during initial emergency operations involving bulk transport vehicle fires? (777)

    A. No lanes

    B. All lanes

    C. At least one lane

    D. At least two lanes

24. Which of the following is the preferred position for fire apparatus during a bulk transport vehicle fire? (777)
    A. Uphill and upwind
    B. Uphill and downwind
    C. Downhill and upwind
    D. Downhill and downwind

25. What is natural gas in its pure form? (778)
    A. Carbon
    B. Butane
    C. Methane
    D. Hydrogen

26. Which of the following statements about natural gas is MOST accurate? (778)
    A. It is lighter than air.
    B. It is heavier than air.
    C. It is nonflammable and toxic.
    D. It is nonflammable and nontoxic.

27. Natural gas is explosive in concentrations: (778)
    A. below 5 percent in air.
    B. above 20 percent in air.
    C. between 5 and 15 percent in air.
    D. between 15 and 20 percent in air.

28. Which of the following is the most widely used type of liquefied petroleum gas (LPG)? (779)
    A. Butane
    B. Propane
    C. Methane
    D. Hydrogen

29. Which of the following statements about liquefied petroleum gas (LPG) is MOST accurate? (779)
    A. Propane is toxic and flammable.
    B. LPG can be used as fuel for motor vehicles.
    C. Propane naturally has a very distinctive odor.
    D. An LPG leak will not produce a visible cloud of vapor.

Firefighter II

_____ 30. Liquefied petroleum gas (LPG) is explosive in concentrations: (779)

    A. greater than 0.5 percent.

    B. greater than 1.5 percent.

    C. between 1.5 and 10 percent.

    D. between 10.5 and 15 percent.

_____ 31. Who should be contacted immediately if there is an incident causing a CNG or LPG supply line to break? (779)

    A. Media

    B. Utility company

    C. Law enforcement personnel

    D. Emergency medical services

_____ 32. Which of the following statements regarding flammable gas incidents is MOST accurate? (779-780)

    A. The first concern is the preservation of evidence.

    B. Hose streams should be used to protect exposures.

    C. If gas is burning, the flame should be extinguished.

    D. Apparatus should approach from the downwind side.

_____ 33. Which of the following is the highest priority for the first engine company? (789)

    A. Protect rescuers.

    B. Assist in extinguishment.

    C. Protect secondary means of egress.

    D. Protect the most threatened exposure.

_____ 34. Two or more fully equipped and immediately available firefighters designated to stand by outside the hazard zone to enter and rescue firefighters inside is known as a(n): (791-792)

    A. first engine company.

    B. second engine company.

    C. Rapid Intervention Crew.

    D. Fireground Support Company.

_____ 35. If the original Incident Commander has the incident well organized and progress is being made toward incident stabilization, a later-arriving chief officer: (792)

    A. leaves the scene entirely.

    B. may choose to assume another role.

    C. must take command of the incident.

    D. must relinquish incident stabilization duties.

Chapter 16

Fire Detection, Alarm, and Suppression Systems

Firefighter I

_____ 1. A system of water pipes, discharge nozzles, and control valves designed to activate during fires by discharging enough water to control a fire is formally known as a(n): (825)
   A. water control system.
   B. automatic sprinkler system.
   C. fire extinguishment system.
   D. downpour discharge system.

_____ 2. Fire pumps and foam extinguishing systems that sense heat, smoke, or gas and activate automatically are known as: (825)
   A. flame control systems.
   B. water control systems.
   C. automatic control systems.
   D. automatic suppression systems.

_____ 3. Which of the following statements about fire detection, alarm, and suppression systems is MOST accurate? (825-826)
   A. Individual systems can only perform one specific function.
   B. Automatic sprinklers are the most reliable fixed fire suppression systems.
   C. Standpipe systems are the most reliable fixed fire suppression systems in industrial occupancies.
   D. About 40% of all fires are controlled by the activation of five or fewer sprinklers.

_____ 4. Sprinklers in an automatic sprinkler system are sometimes called: (842)
   A. sprinkler sets.
   B. watering pipes.
   C. sprinkler heads.
   D. individual setups.

_____ 5. Which of the following is a sprinkler system that protects an entire building? (842)
   A. Partial sprinkler system
   B. Complete sprinkler system
   C. Small-facility sprinkler system
   D. Large-facility sprinkler system

_____ 6. Which of the following is a sprinkler system that only protects high-hazard areas? (842)

    A. Partial sprinkler system

    B. Complete sprinkler system

    C. Small-facility sprinkler system

    D. Large-facility sprinkler system

_____ 7. Which of the following NFPA® standards is used as a guide for installing sprinkler protection in one- and two-family dwellings? (842)

    A. 13A

    B. 13B

    C. 13C

    D. 13D

_____ 8. Which of the following is a reason that a sprinkler system may not perform? (843)

    A. Open water valve

    B. Painted-over sprinklers

    C. Objects stacked far apart

    D. Lack of debris in the pipes

_____ 9. In which of the following situations would sprinklers be MOST effective? (843)

    A. Extremely small fires far away from detection system

    B. Extremely small fires with excessive smoke generation

    C. Sleeping or intoxicated persons occupy the fire building

    D. Protecting lives of occupants in other parts of the building

_____ 10. Where are control valves usually located? (847-848)

    A. Separate from the sprinkler system

    B. Immediately above the sprinkler alarm valve

    C. Outside the building far away from the system they control

    D. Between the source of water supply and the sprinkler system

_____ 11. What is an indicating control valve? (848)

    A. One that stays closed at all times

    B. One that does not indicate whether it is open or closed

    C. One that shows at a glance whether it is open or closed

    D. One that does not need to show whether it is open or closed

12. Which of the following is a type of control valve for a sprinkler system in which the position of the center screw indicates whether the valve is open or closed? (848)
    A. Post indicator valve
    B. Wall post indicator valve
    C. Outside stem and yoke valve
    D. Post indicator valve assembly

13. Which of the following is a type of valve used to control underground water mains and provides a visual means for indicating "open" or "shut"? (848)
    A. Post indicator valve
    B. Wall post indicator valve
    C. Outside stem and yoke valve
    D. Post indicator valve assembly

14. Which of the following extends horizontally through the wall with the target and valve operating nut on the outside of the building? (848)
    A. Post indicator valve
    B. Wall post indicator valve
    C. Outside stem and yoke valve
    D. Post indicator valve assembly

15. Which of the following uses a circular disk inside a flat plate on top of the valve housing to show whether the valve is open or shut? (848)
    A. Post indicator valve
    B. Wall post indicator valve
    C. Outside stem and yoke valve
    D. Post indicator valve assembly

16. Which of the following is provided to simulate the actuation of the system by allowing water to flow into the retard chamber and operate the waterflow alert devices? (848-849)
    A. Post test valve
    B. Alarm test valve
    C. Visual test valve
    D. Operational valve

17. What is the purpose of the inspector's test valve? (849)
    A. To activate the retard chamber
    B. To simulate the activation of all sprinklers
    C. To activate the automatic sprinkler system
    D. To simulate the activation of one sprinkler

_____ 18. What is the primary purpose of the main drain? (850)

    A. To activate the automatic sprinkler system

    B. To simulate the activation of one sprinkler

    C. To allow water to flow into the retard chamber and operate the waterflow alert devices

    D. To allow sprinkler service personnel to drain water from the system for maintenance purposes

_____ 19. How are sprinkler flow alarms normally operated? (850)

    A. Manually

    B. Individually

    C. Mechanically

    D. Hydraulically

_____ 20. Which of the following types of sprinkler systems is the simplest type and generally requires little maintenance? (852)

    A. Dry-pipe

    B. Wet-pipe

    C. Preaction

    D. Residential

_____ 21. Newer wet-pipe systems with a backflow prevention check valve and an electronic flow alarm are sometimes referred to as: (852)

    A. mobile systems.

    B. straight stick systems.

    C. crooked stick systems.

    D. backflow alarm systems.

_____ 22. Which of the following is a chamber that catches excess water that may be sent through the alarm valve during momentary water pressure surges? (852)

    A. Retard chamber

    B. Holding chamber

    C. Water surge chamber

    D. Alarm valve overflow chamber

_____ 23. Which of the following is a fire-suppression system that consists of closed sprinklers attached to a piping system that contains air under pressure? (853)

    A. Dry-pipe

    B. Wet-pipe

    C. Deluge

    D. Residential

24. The required air pressure for dry-pipe systems is usually about: (853)
    A. 20 psi (140 kPa) above the trip pressure.
    B. 20 psi (140 kPa) below the trip pressure.
    C. 40 psi (280 kPa) above the trip pressure.
    D. 40 psi (280 kPa) below the trip pressure.

25. Dry systems that employ a deluge-type valve, fire detection devices, and closed sprinklers are known as: (854)
    A. deluge systems.
    B. preaction systems.
    C. residential systems.
    D. closed detection systems.

26. Which of the following types of systems are used when it is especially important to prevent water damage, even if pipes are broken? (854)
    A. Deluge systems
    B. Wet-pipe systems
    C. Preaction systems
    D. Residential systems

27. The system similar to dry-pipe systems in that there is no water in the distribution piping before system activation but different in that it has no fusible links is a: (854)
    A. deluge system.
    B. wet-pipe system.
    C. preaction system.
    D. residential system.

28. In a deluge system, all sprinklers: (854)
    A. are open all the time.
    B. are closed all the time.
    C. require someone to open them manually.
    D. require an electrical system to control opening/closing.

29. In which of the following locations would a deluge system MOST likely be present? (855)
    A. Grocery store
    B. Aircraft hangar
    C. Apartment complex
    D. Single-family residence

_____ 30. Which of the following systems is covered by NFPA®13D and may be either a wet- or dry-pipe system? (855)
- A. Deluge system
- B. Preaction system
- C. Residential system
- D. Industrial occupancy system

_____ 31. The point at which the fire department can connect into a sprinkler or standpipe system to boost the water flow in the system is known as the: (856)
- A. sprinkler water connection.
- B. standpipe boost connection.
- C. Fire Department Connection.
- D. Water Flow Extension System.

_____ 32. Which of the following statements about operations at fires in protected properties is MOST accurate? (856)
- A. Sprinkler system control valves must be closed.
- B. Premature closure of the control valve has no effect on fire.
- C. Firefighters may be required to stop the flow of water from a single sprinkler.
- D. All departments shut the entire system down by closing the main control valve.

_____ 1. A common term for the most basic alarm system is: (826)
- A. alert system.
- B. fire detection system.
- C. water control system.
- D. local warning system.

_____ 2. The temperature of the surrounding environment is known as: (827)
- A. climate.
- B. weather.
- C. normal temperature.
- D. ambient temperature.

_____ 3. Where are heat detectors normally installed? (827)
- A. In the back of a room
- B. In the front of a room
- C. In the lowest portions of a room
- D. In the highest portions of a room

_____ 4. A temperature-sensitive device that senses temperature changes and sounds an alarm at a specific point is a(n): (827)
- A. no-temperature heat detector.
- B. fixed-temperature heat detector.
- C. temperature change heat detector.
- D. ambient-temperature heat detector.

_____ 5. A small glass vial fitted into the discharge orifice of a fire sprinkler is the: (827)
- A. fusible device.
- B. frangible bulb.
- C. two-piece link.
- D. resistance indicator.

_____ 6. The two-piece link held together with a metal that melts or fuses at a specific temperature is a: (827)
- A. standard link.
- B. fusible device.
- C. frangible bulb.
- D. resistance indicator.

Firefighter II

_____ 7. Which of the following types of heat detectors can detect heat over a linear area parallel to the detector? (828)
   A. Bimetallic detector
   B. Continuous line detector
   C. Rate-of-rise heat detector
   D. Rate compensated detector

_____ 8. Which of the following types of heat detectors uses two metals that have different thermal expansion characteristics? (828)
   A. Bimetallic detector
   B. Continuous line detector
   C. Rate-of-rise heat detector
   D. Pneumatic rate-of-rise spot detector

_____ 9. A temperature-sensitive device that sounds an alarm when the temperature changes at a preset value is a: (829)
   A. bimetallic detector.
   B. continuous line detector.
   C. rate-of-rise heat detector.
   D. hydraulic rate-of-rise spot detector.

_____ 10. Which of the following is the most common type of rate-of-rise heat detectors? (829)
   A. Rate-compensated detector
   B. Hydraulic rate-of-rise spot detector
   C. Pneumatic rate-of-rise line detector
   D. Pneumatic rate-of-rise spot detector

_____ 11. Which of the following types of heat detectors monitors a large area surrounding its location? (830)
   A. Thermoelectric detector
   B. Rate-compensated detector
   C. Pneumatic rate-of-rise line detector
   D. Pneumatic rate-of-rise spot detector

_____ 12. The detector designed for use in areas normally subject to regular temperature changes that are slower than those under fire conditions is a: (830)
   A. thermoelectric detector.
   B. rate-compensated detector.
   C. pneumatic rate-of-rise line detector.
   D. pneumatic rate-of-rise spot detector.

_____ 13. The rate-of-rise detector that operates on the principle that when two wires of dissimilar metals are twisted together and heated at one end, an electrical current is generated at the other end is the: (830)

A. thermoelectric detector.

B. rate-compensated detector.

C. pneumatic rate-of-rise line detector.

D. pneumatic rate-of-rise spot detector.

_____ 14. Which of the following is an alarm-initiating device designed to actuate when visible or invisible products of combustion are present in the space? (831)

A. Smoke alarm

B. Smoke detector

C. Visibility alarm

D. Visibility detector

_____ 15. A device designed to sound an alarm when the products of combustion are present in the room where the device is installed is a (n): (831)

A. smoke alarm.

B. smoke detector.

C. alarm indicating device.

D. combustion detection alert.

_____ 16. Which of the following is a type of smoke detector that uses a small light source to detect smoke by shining light through the detector's chamber? (832)

A. Light-based smoke detector

B. Photoelectric smoke detector

C. Light sensitivity smoke alarm

D. Refractory application smoke alarm

_____ 17. Which of the following types of smoke detectors uses a beam of light that focuses across the area being monitored and onto a photoelectric cell? (832)

A. Beam application

B. Refractory photocell

C. Light application beam

D. Visibility-based light beam

Firefighter II

_____ 18. Which of the following types of smoke detectors uses a light beam that passes through a small chamber at a point away from the light source? (832)

A. Beam application

B. Refractory photocell

C. Light application beam

D. Visibility-based light beam

_____ 19. The type of smoke detector that uses a small amount of radioactive material to make the air within a sensing chamber conduct electricity is the: (833)

A. ionization detector.

B. ion/current detector.

C. electricity-based detector.

D. beta particle energy detector.

_____ 20. Which of the following detectors generally responds faster to flaming fires than smoldering ones and automatically resets when the atmosphere has cleared? (833)

A. Ionization detector

B. Thermoelectric detector

C. Rate-compensated detector

D. Pneumatic rate-of-rise spot detector

_____ 21. An alarm device used in some fire detection systems that detects light in the ultraviolet wave spectrum is a(n): (834)

A. light detector.

B. flame detector.

C. ultraviolet wave alarm.

D. light-sensing flame alarm.

_____ 22. Which of the following is NOT one of the three basic types of flame detectors? (834)

A. Those that detect no light

B. Those that detect only UV light

C. Those that detect only IR light

D. Those that detect UV and IR light

_____ 23. A device used to detect gases produced by a fire within a confined space is a: (835)

A. fire-gas detector.

B. confined gas alarm.

C. combination detector.

D. fuel-contaminant alarm.

24. Which of the following is an alarm-initiating device capable of detecting an abnormal condition by more than one means? (835)
    A. Fire-gas detector
    B. Confined gas alarm
    C. Combination detector
    D. Fuel-contaminant alarm

25. An alarm actuated by heat, gas, smoke, or waterflow in a sprinkler system conveyed to local alarm bells or the fire station is a(n): (837)
    A. preset alarm.
    B. automatic alarm.
    C. self-actuated alarm.
    D. fire station notification alarm.

26. What is a local energy system? (837)
    A. An alarm system that does not interconnect with a municipal alarm circuit
    B. An alarm system in which the municipal alarm circuit extends into the protected property
    C. An alarm system that is connected to the fire department communication center through an answering service
    D. An auxiliary alarm system within an occupancy that is attached directly to a hard-wired municipal fire alarm master box

27. What is a shunt system? (838)
    A. An alarm system that does not interconnect with a municipal alarm circuit
    B. An alarm system in which the municipal alarm circuit extends into the protected property
    C. An alarm system that is connected to the fire department communication center through an answering service
    D. An auxiliary alarm system within an occupancy that is attached directly to a hard-wired municipal fire alarm master box

28. What is a parallel telephone system? (838)
    A. An alarm system that does not interconnect with a municipal alarm circuit
    B. An alarm system in which the municipal alarm circuit extends into the protected property
    C. An alarm system that is connected to the fire department communication center through an answering service
    D. An auxiliary alarm system within an occupancy that is attached directly to a hard-wired municipal fire alarm master box

16

_____ 29. What is a remote station system? (838)
- A. An alarm system that does not interconnect with a municipal alarm circuit
- B. An alarm system in which the municipal alarm circuit extends into the protected property
- C. An alarm system that is connected to the fire department communication center through an answering service
- D. An auxiliary alarm system within an occupancy that is attached directly to a hard-wired municipal fire alarm master box

_____ 30. When is a non-coded system allowable? (838)
- A. In all circumstances and under all conditions
- B. Only in circumstances decided by the fire marshal
- C. Where a single occupancy is protected by the system
- D. Where an apartment complex is protected by the system

_____ 31. A fire protection system owned and operated by the property owner is commonly known as a(n): (839)
- A. central station system.
- B. proprietary alarm system.
- C. automatic protection system.
- D. municipally protected system.

_____ 32. Which of the following types of systems is owned by the property owner but is monitored at an off-site, contracted service point? (839-840)
- A. Central station system
- B. Proprietary alarm system
- C. Automatic protection system
- D. Municipally protected system

_____ 33. Which of the following statements about supervising fire alarm systems is MOST accurate? (840-841)
- A. Fire alarm systems are designed to be supervised by an engineer.
- B. The control panel must be specifically listed by a testing laboratory for its purpose.
- C. Fixed fire suppression systems depend solely on a signal from a manual pull station.
- D. Many older systems operated with open, unsupervised circuits in which current flowed sporadically.

_____ 34. An alarm that sounds before a total flooding fire extinguishing system is about to discharge is known as a: (841)
- A. flooding detector.
- B. predischarge alarm.
- C. disaster-aversion sounding.
- D. discharge notification signal.

35. Which of the following statements regarding auxiliary services is MOST accurate? (842)
    A. Fire alarm systems hinder evacuation.
    B. Fire detection systems cannot override elevator controls.
    C. Fire detection systems detect toxic and combustible gases.
    D. The primary objective of a fire alarm system is to alert the media.

36. A vertical water pipe used to carry water for fire protection systems above ground is a: (844)
    A. riser.
    B. carry.
    C. supplier.
    D. water lift.

37. What pipe connects the riser to the cross mains? (844)
    A. Feed main
    B. Branch main
    C. Water rise pipe
    D. Cross connection pipe

38. Which of the following components directly service a number of branch lines on which the sprinklers are installed? (844)
    A. Heads
    B. Risers
    C. Feed mains
    D. Cross mains

39. The waterflow device in a sprinkler system is known as a: (845)
    A. link.
    B. bulb.
    C. pellet.
    D. sprinkler.

40. Which of the following components holds the levers together until the link is melted by the heat of a fire? (845)
    A. Sprinkler
    B. Fusible link
    C. Chemical pellet
    D. Frangible bulb

Firefighter II

_____ 41. A small nodule filled with liquid and an air bubble to hold the orifice shut is a: (846)

    A. sprinkler.

    B. fusible link.

    C. chemical pellet.

    D. frangible bulb.

_____ 42. Which of the following sprinkler components allows a plunger to move down and release the valve cap parts? (846)

    A. Sprinkler

    B. Fusible link

    C. Chemical pellet

    D. Frangible bulb

_____ 43. The most common type of sprinkler is the: (846)

    A. upright.

    B. pendant.

    C. sidewall.

    D. special-purpose.

_____ 44. The sprinkler that screws into the top of the piping and discharges water into a solid deflector that breaks it into a hemispherical spray pattern directed at the floor is the: (846)

    A. upright sprinkler.

    B. pendant sprinkler.

    C. sidewall sprinkler.

    D. special-purpose sprinkler.

_____ 45. The sprinkler that extends from the side of a pipe and is used in small rooms where the branch line runs along a wall is a(n): (847)

    A. upright sprinkler.

    B. pendant sprinkler.

    C. sidewall sprinkler.

    D. special-purpose sprinkler.

_____ 46. Which of the following types of sprinklers includes those with corrosive-resistant coatings? (847)

    A. Upright

    B. Pendant

    C. Sidewall

    D. Special-purpose

47. A minimum water supply has to deliver the required volume of water to the highest sprinkler in a building at a residual pressure of: (850)
   A. 10 psi (70 kPa).
   B. 15 psi (105 kPa).
   C. 20 psi (140 kPa).
   D. 25 psi (175 kPa).

48. Sprinkler fire department connections should be supplied with water from pumpers that have a capacity of at least: (851)
   A. 1,000 gpm (4 000 L/min).
   B. 1,500 gpm (6 000 L/min).
   C. 2,000 gpm (8 000 L/min).
   D. 2,500 gpm (10 000 L/min).

49. The sprinkler system that is the simplest and requires little maintenance is the: (852)
   A. dry-pipe.
   B. wet-pipe.
   C. preaction.
   D. residential.

50. Which of the following is a newer wet-pipe system with a backflow prevention check valve and an electronic flow alarm? (852)
   A. Mobile systems
   B. Straight stick systems
   C. Crooked stick systems
   D. Backflow alarm systems

51. The chamber that catches excess water that may be sent through the alarm valve during momentary water pressure surges is the: (852)
   A. retard chamber.
   B. holding chamber.
   C. water surge chamber.
   D. alarm valve overflow chamber.

52. The fire-suppression system that consists of closed sprinklers attached to a piping system that contains air under pressure is known as a: (853)
   A. dry-pipe system.
   B. wet-pipe system.
   C. deluge system.
   D. residential system.

53. What is usually the required air pressure for dry-pipe systems? (853)
    A. 20 psi (140 kPa) above the trip pressure
    B. 20 psi (140 kPa) below the trip pressure
    C. 40 psi (280 kPa) above the trip pressure
    D. 40 psi (280 kPa) below the trip pressure

54. Which of the following is a dry system that employs a deluge-type valve, fire detection devices, and closed sprinklers? (854)
    A. Deluge systems
    B. Preaction systems
    C. Residential systems
    D. Closed detection systems

55. Which of the following types of systems is used when it is especially important to prevent water damage, even if pipes are broken? (854)
    A. Deluge systems
    B. Wet-pipe systems
    C. Preaction systems
    D. Residential systems

56. The system similar to dry-pipe systems in that there is no water in the distribution piping before system activation but different in that it has no fusible links is a: (854)
    A. deluge system.
    B. wet-pipe system.
    C. preaction system.
    D. residential system.

57. In a deluge system, all sprinklers: (854)
    A. are open all the time.
    B. are closed all the time.
    C. require someone to open them manually.
    D. require an electrical system to control opening/closing.

58. In which of the following locations would a deluge system MOST likely be present? (855)
    A. Grocery store
    B. Aircraft hangar
    C. Apartment complex
    D. Single-family residence

Firefighter II

_____ 59. The system covered by NFPA® 13D which may be either a wet- or dry-pipe system is a(n): (855)

    A. deluge system.

    B. preaction system.

    C. residential system.

    D. industrial occupancy system.

Firefighter II

Firefighter I

_____ 1. Which of the following statements BEST describes the philosophy of loss control? (868)

    A. To minimize negative public relations stemming from an incident

    B. To maximize positive public relations and downplay any losses sustained by the public

    C. To focus on minimizing losses only during operations and let other agencies provide customer support when losses occur

    D. To minimize damage and provide customer service through effective mitigation and recovery efforts before, during, and after an incident

_____ 2. Which of the following consists of those operations associated with fire fighting that aid in reducing primary and secondary damage during fire fighting operations? (869)

    A. Salvage

    B. Overhaul

    C. Protective actions

    D. Offensive procedures

_____ 3. Which of the following consists of those operations involved in searching for and extinguishing hidden or remaining fires? (869)

    A. Salvage

    B. Overhaul

    C. Protective actions

    D. Defensive operations

_____ 4. Which of the following refers to damage caused by the fire? (869)

    A. Initial damage

    B. Primary damage

    C. Secondary damage

    D. Tertiary damage

_____ 5. Which of the following refers to damage that is caused by suppression activities? (869)

    A. Initial damage

    B. Primary damage

    C. Secondary damage

    D. Tertiary damage

_____ 6. Salvage starts as soon as adequate personnel are available and: (869)

    A. may not be started until the fire is considered extinguished.

    B. may not be started until fire cause has been determined.

    C. may be done until the fire scene investigator authorizes it.

    D. may be done simultaneously with fire attack if resources permit.

_____ 7. Overhaul operations should be delayed until: (869)

    A. the fire is considered at least 50% contained.

    B. the fire is considered at least 75% contained.

    C. the fire scene investigator authorizes overhaul operations.

    D. the initial fire attack has been completed and risk is minimized.

_____ 8. Why are protecting computers and filing cabinets containing documents such as accounts receivable important in commercial occupancies? (869)

    A. These items are often not insured.

    B. These items are often very expensive.

    C. These are often vital to business survival.

    D. These items often provide clues to fire cause.

_____ 9. What should be developed for buildings with high-value contents that are especially susceptible to water and smoke damage? (869)

    A. Special preincident plans

    B. Special prepayment for services plans

    C. Waiver of liability forms for fire departments

    D. Statement of additional insurance to cover contents

_____ 10. Fire departments can facilitate salvage efforts before a fire incident by working with: (870)

    A. local and state insurance representatives.

    B. local union representatives for businesses.

    C. the building code enforcement representative for their area.

    D. the loss-control representatives of various local businesses.

_____ 11. How should household furnishings be grouped when arranging for salvage? (870)

    A. By a doorway or exit

    B. In the center of the room

    C. Lined on the edges of the room

    D. In an X-shaped pattern at one end of the room

_____ 12. How should stock be stored so that it is less vulnerable to water damage? (871)

    A. On pallets

    B. In plastic tubs

    C. Covered by tarps

    D. Sealed in containers

_____ 13. Why should cabinets and tabletops be wiped off with disposable paper towels? (872)

    A. Water left on cabinets and other horizontal surfaces may be a slipping hazard.

    B. Water left on cabinets and other horizontal surfaces may make it difficult to find hidden fires.

    C. Water left on cabinets and other horizontal surfaces may make it difficult to pinpoint fire cause.

    D. Water left on cabinets and other horizontal surfaces may ruin finishes over a period of hours.

_____ 14. Which of the following is a characteristic of synthetic salvage covers? (872)

    A. Lightweight

    C. Difficult to handle

    B. Relatively expensive

    D. For indoor use only

_____ 15. Ordinarily, the only cleaning required for canvas salvage covers is: (873)

    A. placing in a commercial salvage cover washer.

    B. shaking the salvage covers to remove particles.

    C. spraying with a mixture of water and harsh detergents.

    D. wetting or rinsing with a hose stream and scrubbing with a broom.

_____ 16. Which of the following statements about synthetic salvage covers is MOST accurate? (873)

    A. Synthetic salvage covers require more maintenance than canvas salvage covers.

    B. Synthetic salvage covers require less maintenance than canvas salvage covers.

    C. Synthetic and canvas salvage covers have the same maintenance requirements.

    D. Synthetic salvage covers initially have more maintenance but over time require less maintenance than canvas salvage covers.

_____ 17. What should be done with salvage covers if they are found to have holes? (873)

    A. They should be discarded.

    B. They should be repaired.

    C. They should be used only for training purposes.

    D. They should be used only on less valuable contents.

_____ 18. Where should salvage equipment be located for conducting salvage operations at a fire? (873)

    A. In the fire station

    B. In a readily accessible area on the apparatus

    C. In a readily accessible area at the Command Post

    D. In the vehicle driven by the fire investigator

_____ 19. The tools in an automatic sprinkler kit are used to: (875)

    A. stop the flow of water from an open sprinkler.

    B. start the flow of water from a closed sprinkler.

    C. supplement the nozzle hoses used to extinguish a fire.

    D. help extinguish very small nuisance or smoldering fires.

_____ 20. Which of the following are used to carry debris, catch falling debris, and provide a water basin for immersing small burning objects? (876)

    A. Carryalls

    B. Floor runners

    C. Trash-type pumps

    D. Water barrels

_____ 21. Which of the following are used to protect floor coverings from mud and grime tracked in by firefighters? (876)

    A. Carryalls

    B. Floor runners

    C. Trash-type pumps

    D. Water barrels

_____ 22. Which of the following dewatering devices are best suited for salvage operations? (876)

    A. Water barrels

    B. Trash-type pumps

    C. Fire department pumpers

    D. Reverse-suction pumpers

_____ 23. Which of the following are designed to be driven into walls or wooden framing to provide a strong point from which to hang items such as salvage covers? (877)

    A. A-hooks

    B. J-hooks

    C. S-hooks

    D. O-hooks

24. Which of the following cannot be driven into walls or framing but must have a horizontal ledge from which to hang? (877)
    A. A-hooks
    B. J-hooks
    C. S-hooks
    D. O-hooks

25. Which of the following spreads has the principal advantage of one person being able to quickly unroll a cover across the top of an object and unfold it? (878)
    A. One-firefighter spread with a rolled salvage cover
    B. One-firefighter spread with a folded salvage cover
    C. One-firefighter spread with a boxed salvage cover
    D. One-firefighter spread with an opened salvage cover

26. Which of the following is the most common method for two firefighters to deploy a large salvage cover? (879)
    A. Tent throw
    B. Balloon throw
    C. Circus spread
    D. Flat roll and carry

27. Water chutes may be constructed to drain runoff through windows or doors on the: (879)
    A. same floor as fire fighting operations.
    B. floor below fire fighting operations.
    C. floor above fire fighting operations.
    D. adjacent floor to fire fighting operations.

28. Which of the following is used to construct a catchall? (879)
    A. Carryall
    B. Hoseline
    C. Water barrel
    D. Salvage cover

29. When objects are too large to be covered by a single cover it will be necessary to: (880)
    A. find a larger cover.
    B. splice covers with water-tight joints.
    C. use two covers and overlap the ends.
    D. allow part of the object to remain exposed.

_____ 30. One of the final parts of salvage operations is: (880)

    A. determining the cause of the fire.

    B. recognizing and preserving evidence of arson.

    C. searching for and extinguishing hidden or remaining fires.

    D. the covering of openings to prevent further damage to the property by weather.

_____ 31. Which of the following is NOT an operation performed during overhaul? (881)

    A. Determining the cause of the fire

    B. Recognizing and preserving evidence of arson

    C. Searching for and extinguishing hidden or remaining fire

    D. Covering property to protect it from exposure during fire fighting operations

_____ 32. Which of the following is one of the most common and most dangerous threats to firefighters during overhaul operations? (881)

    A. Backdraft

    B. Flashover

    C. Toxic gas

    D. Intense heat from flames

_____ 33. Which of the following must be a routine part of the overhaul operation? (881)

    A. Estimating clean-up costs

    B. Wearing loose, comfortable clothing

    C. Determining appropriate mode of fire attack

    D. Wearing appropriate PPE, including respiratory protection

_____ 34. Which of the following overhaul tools and equipment are used to open ceilings to check on fire extension? (882)

    A. Axes

    B. Prying tools

    C. Pike poles and plaster hooks

    D. Power saws, drills, and screwdrivers

_____ 35. Which of the following overhaul tools and equipment are used to open walls and floors? (882)

    A. Axes

    B. Prying tools

    C. Pike poles and plaster hooks

    D. Power saws, drills, and screwdrivers

_____ 36. Which of the following is a safety consideration during overhaul operations? (883)
    A. Continue to work in teams of two or more.
    B. Disconnect all attack lines used in initial operations.
    C. Wear loose, comfortable clothing to avoid overheating.
    D. Maintain a RIC until overhaul operations are well underway.

_____ 37. Which of the following would be an indicator of possible loss of structural integrity? (883)
    A. Water pooled on lower floors
    B. Large quantities of fire debris
    C. Concrete that has spalled due to heat
    D. Windows and doors that have shattered glass

_____ 38. Which of the following is an indicator of a possible hidden fire? (883-884)
    A. Popping or cracking of fire burning
    B. Absence of sound from a particular area
    C. Doors that have become partially open
    D. Areas that appear visually unaffected by the fire

_____ 39. Where does overhaul typically begin? (884)
    A. In the most easily accessible area
    B. Either in the basement or on the roof
    C. In the area of least severe fire involvement
    D. In the area of most severe fire involvement

_____ 40. Which of the following statements about insulation materials is MOST accurate? (884)
    A. Usually it is necessary to remove the material in order to properly check it or extinguish fire in it.
    B. Usually the material does not need to be removed and can be checked or fire extinguished in it in the structure.
    C. Insulation materials are generally fire retardant and thus cannot harbor hidden fires.
    D. Insulation materials are generally self-extinguishing so are not a hidden fire concern.

_____ 41. When concealed spaces below floors, above ceilings, or within walls and partitions must be opened during the search for hidden fires: (885)
    A. remove as much of the wall, ceiling, or floor covering as possible.
    B. remove weight-bearing members so complete extinguishment is ensured.
    C. remove only an area that is only large enough to put a hoseline through it.
    D. remove only enough wall, ceiling, or floor covering to ensure complete extinguishment.

_____ 42. Which of the following is the MOST effective way to extinguish small burning objects uncovered during overhaul? (885)
  A. Dump buckets of water on them.
  B. Drench them with hose streams.
  C. Throw salvage covers on top of them.
  D. Submerge entire objects in containers of water.   .

_____ 43. Which of the following is the MOST effective way to extinguish larger furnishings, such as mattresses and stuffed furniture, during overhaul? (885-886)
  A. Dump buckets of water on them.
  B. Throw salvage covers on top of them.
  C. Submerge entire objects in containers of water.
  D. Remove them to the outside where they can be thoroughly extinguished.

_____ 44. The use of wetting agents such as Class A foam: (886)
  A. should not be used during overhaul.
  B. can cause reignition of hidden fires.
  C. can be used during overhaul but not on upholstery.
  D. is of considerable value when extinguishing hidden fires.

_____ 45. Which of the following is the only way to ensure that fires in bales of rags, cotton, hay, etc. are completely out? (886)
  A. Break them apart.
  B. Drench them with hose streams.
  C. Throw salvage covers on top of them.
  D. Use hand-held portable extinguishers on them.

_____ 1. Who has the legal responsibility for determining the cause and origin of a fire in most jurisdictions? (910)
   A. The fire chief
   B. The police chief
   C. State Fire Marshall's office
   D. State Insurance Examiner's office

_____ 2. Which of the following may indicate an incendiary fire and should be noted by first-arriving firefighters? (910)
   A. Status of doors and windows (locked or open)
   B. Direction that smoke is blowing from the structure
   C. Mail and/or newspapers that have not been taken inside
   D. Absence of any landscaping or outdoor decorations

_____ 3. Which of the following terms refers to the exact physical location where the heat source and fuel come in contact with each other and a fire begins? (910)
   A. Flashpoint
   B. Point of origin
   C. Autoignition point
   D. Point of combustion

_____ 4. Which of the following is the MOST accurate statement about people and a fire scene? (911)
   A. Most people will immediately leave a fire scene.
   B. Anyone at the fire scene is probably involved in setting the fire.
   C. Whether or not people are at the scene is not a concern to firefighters.
   D. Most people are intrigued by a fire and will remain in the area to watch.

_____ 5. Why might arsonists set fires during inclement weather? (911)
   A. They are less likely to be apprehended.
   B. The fire is likely to be easier to start.
   C. The fire is more likely to be ruled accidental.
   D. The fire department's response may be delayed.

Firefighter I

6. What should firefighters do before opening doors and windows? (911)
   A. Determine that no occupants are inside of the building
   B. Determine that opening the door or window will not set off any alarms
   C. Determine that opening the door or window will cause expensive damage
   D. Determine whether they are locked, unlocked, or show any signs of forced entry

7. Which of the following terms refers to combustible material used to spread fire from one area to another? (912)
   A. Trailer
   B. Pulley
   C. Connector
   D. Arson train

8. Why should firefighters note the presence of metal or plastic containers found inside or outside the structure? (912)
   A. They contribute to overall fire load.
   B. They may contain fire extinguishing agents.
   C. They may have been used to break into the facility.
   D. They may have been used to transport accelerants.

9. Which of the following is MOST likely to indicate possible accelerant use? (912)
   A. Several rekindles in the same area
   B. Only one possible point of origin
   C. Smoke that rises more quickly than usual
   D. Flammable décor near the point of origin

10. Water applied to a burning liquid accelerant may cause it to splatter, allowing flame intensity to: (912)
    A. increase and the fire to spread in several directions.
    B. decrease and the fire to remain contained in one area.
    C. initially increase and then the fire to self-extinguish.
    D. initially decrease but then increase and spread in several directions.

11. Which of the following statements about incendiary devices is MOST accurate? (913)
    A. Most incendiary devices leave evidence of their existence.
    B. Most incendiary devices do not leave evidence of their existence.
    C. Most incendiary devices are homemade and generally not able to start fires.
    D. Special sensory equipment is needed to pick up evidence of most incendiary devices.

_____ 12. Why is it important to note any structural alterations? (913)
  A. They may be in violation of building codes.
  B. They may be used by occupants to hide or stash illegal items.
  C. They will determine whether an offensive or defensive approach is taken.
  D. They can be used to allow a fire to spread quickly through the structure.

_____ 13. Which of the following may indicate that the fire was intentionally set? (914)
  A. Major household items that are relatively new
  B. Important papers and items being locked in a fire safe
  C. Insurance policies or legal documents being lost in the fire
  D. Absence of items of sentimental value such as photo albums

_____ 14. Which of the following is LEAST likely to be able to be determined from the fire's movement and intensity patterns? (914)
  A. The fuel(s) involved
  B. How the fire spread
  C. The original ignition source
  D. The cost of fire extinguishment

_____ 15. Which of the following personnel usually interrogates a potential arson suspect? (914)
  A. District attorney
  B. Senior firefighter
  C. Fire investigator
  D. First-arriving firefighter

_____ 16. Which of the following statements about owners or occupants of a property is MOST accurate? (914)
  A. They should be allowed to talk freely if they are inclined to do so.
  B. They should not be allowed to talk freely without a lawyer present.
  C. They should immediately be considered a suspect and interrogated.
  D. They should be allowed to make statements to the media but not fire department personnel.

_____ 17. To whom should firefighters make statements to regarding the fire? (915)
  A. Fire investigator
  B. Other firefighters
  C. Media personnel
  D. Property owners or occupants

_____ 18. Which of the following would be the MOST appropriate response for a firefighter regarding a question about fire cause? (915)

    A. The fire is under investigation.

    B. It was obviously an intentional fire.

    C. We are pretty sure we know who did it.

    D. I think it was set by the building owner for insurance.

_____ 19. Any public statement regarding the fire cause should be made only after: (915)

    A. an arrest has been made in the case.

    B. all salvage and overhaul operations are completed.

    C. media personnel have been briefed on the incident.

    D. the investigator and ranking fire officer have agreed to its accuracy and validity.

_____ 20. Which of the following statements about documenting personal observations is MOST accurate? (916)

    A. Firefighters should compare observations with other crew members to aid in documentation.

    B. All firefighter documentation and personal observations should be made available to media personnel.

    C. Documentation of personal observations can be done well after the incident as firefighters have down time.

    D. Firefighters should not discuss their observations with other crew members until after documentation is complete.

_____ 21. Why is having a written account of observations during an incident important? (916)

    A. It is required under NIMS-ICS.

    B. Firefighters may have to testify in court.

    C. It is required to file any insurance claims.

    D. It prevents the fire department from having any liability.

_____ 22. When should overhaul operations begin? (916)

    A. As soon as personnel become available.

    B. After salvage operations are considered complete.

    C. After the origin and cause of the fire have been determined.

    D. Overhaul operations can be started simultaneously with fire attack.

_____ 23. When does the fire department have the authority to deny access to a building? (916)

    A. The fire department does not have the authority to deny access to a building.

    B. Only during fire fighting operations until the fire is considered extinguished.

    C. The fire department can deny access to a building at their discretion for any length of time.

    D. During fire fighting operations and for a reasonable length of time after a fire suppression is terminated

____ 24. What may be required to reenter the premises once all fire personnel have left the scene? (916)
  A. Nothing is required
  B. A search warrant
  C. Statement of need
  D. Law enforcement escort

____ 25. What is needed for an individual who is not a fire department employee to enter the fire scene? (916)
  A. Nothing is required
  B. Fire investigator's permission
  C. Permission from any firefighter
  D. Media pass showing identification

____ 26. What should be done if partially burned papers are found in a furnace, stove, or fireplace? (918)
  A. They should be drenched with hose streams.
  B. They should be completely extinguished and shoveled into debris piles.
  C. They should be protected by immediately opening dampers and other openings.
  D. They should be protected by immediately closing dampers and other openings.

____ 27. Which of the following statements about protecting and preserving evidence is MOST accurate? (918)
  A. Firefighters should move all evidence to the fire station.
  B. Firefighters are not responsible for evidence preservation.
  C. Once evidence has been handled by firefighters it is no longer admissible in court.
  D. Firefighters should avoid gathering or handling evidence unless absolutely necessary.

____ 28. Which of the following is the BEST way to preserve human footprints? (918)
  A. Place a cardboard box over them
  B. Place a salvage cover on top of them
  C. Place a large sheet of paper over them
  D. Place caution tape in the shape of an X over them

Protecting Fire Scene Evidence

Firefighter II

_____ 1. In most jurisdictions the legal responsibility for determining the cause and origin of a fire is given to the: (910)

A. fire chief.

B. police chief.

C. insurance investigator.

D. homeowner's association.

_____ 2. Which of the following personnel are in the BEST position to observe unusual conditions that may indicate an incendiary fire? (910)

A. Media personnel

B. Second-due firefighters

C. First-arriving firefighters

D. Nearby neighbors and bystanders

_____ 3. In many departments, fire investigators are also sworn peace officers who: (910)

A. work part-time for the police department.

B. are authorized to carry weapons and make arrests.

C. act as a liaison between the fire and police departments.

D. act as a liaison between the media and the fire department.

_____ 4. Which of the following observations related to time of day would MOST likely be an observation that firefighters would want to notice and gather information on? (910-911)

A. Building clocks and appliances set to the correct time

B. Employees in an office building well after working hours

C. Occupants asleep between the hours of 10 p.m. and 6 a.m.

D. All lights are turned off if it the building is normally unoccupied or residents are asleep

_____ 5. Which of the following would be the MOST important item to notice on a vehicle speeding away from a fire scene? (911)

A. Direction of travel

B. License plate number

C. Whether occupants were buckled

D. Whether windows were up or down

_____ 6. Which of the following is MOST likely to be done in order to delay discovery of a fire? (911)

    A. Closing window curtains or blinds

    B. Closing all doors and windows

    C. Using deadbolt locks in addition to locks on the doorknob

    D. Covering insides of windows with blankets, paint, or paper

_____ 7. Which of the following is an important observation to make upon arrival at a fire scene? (911)

    A. Wind chill and humidity

    B. Wind direction and velocity

    C. Humidity and barometric pressure

    D. Barometric pressure and temperature

_____ 8. Which of the following terms refers to a combustible material used to spread fire from one area to another? (912)

    A. Trailer

    B. Accelerant

    C. Ignition runner

    D. Combustion tool

_____ 9. Which of the following is the MOST likely to indicate possible accelerant use? (912)

    A. White, thin smoke

    B. Dark smoke that rises suddenly

    C. Sudden decrease in flame intensity

    D. Several rekindles in the same area

_____ 10. Which of the following refers to material or chemicals designed and used to start a fire? (913)

    A. Trailer

    B. Incendiary device

    C. Ignition device

    D. Combustion point

_____ 11. Which of the following structural alterations may be done to allow a fire to spread quickly through a structure? (913)

    A. Doors nailed shut

    B. Furniture placed in doorways

    C. Furniture piled in the middle of a room

    D. Removal of plaster or drywall to expose wood

12. Evidence of high heat intensity may indicate the use of accelerants or: (914)
    A. intentionally disconnected gas lines.
    B. intentionally disconnected electrical lines.
    C. intentionally disconnected phone lines.
    D. intentionally disconnected surveillance cameras.

13. If fire detection and suppression systems and devices are inoperable firefighters should check for: (914)
    A. service dates on the equipment.
    B. correct initial installation of equipment.
    C. evidence of tampering or intentional damage.
    D. overdue bills for servicing/maintaining the equipment.

14. Which of the following fire locations is MOST likely to cause firefighters to take notice? (914)
    A. Fires in file drawers
    B. Fires near cooking areas
    C. Fires in main living area
    D. Fires in sleeping areas

15. Which of the following is MOST likely to indicate that the fire was intentionally set? (914)
    A. Major household items that are higher end brands
    B. Insurance policies or legal documents being lost in the fire
    C. Important papers and items being kept in a bank safety deposit box
    D. Absence of personal possessions such as diplomas and financial papers

16. A potential arson suspect is usually interrogated by a: (914)
    A. fire chief.
    B. fire investigator.
    C. senior firefighter.
    D. district attorney.

17. Which of the following statements about owners or occupants of a property is MOST accurate? (914)
    A. They should be allowed to talk freely if they are inclined to do so.
    B. They should immediately be considered a suspect and placed under arrest.
    C. They must have a lawyer present when making any statements about the fire.
    D. They should be allowed to make statements to the media but not fire department personnel.

Firefighter II

18. Firefighters should make statements of their opinions regarding the fire to: (915)
    A. other firefighters.
    B. media personnel.
    C. the fire investigator.
    D. property owners or occupants.

19. Which of the following would be the MOST appropriate response for a firefighter regarding a question about fire cause? (915)
    A. That is not any of your business.
    B. My opinion is that it was arson.
    C. The fire is under investigation.
    D. The fire was probably intentional.

20. Any public statement regarding the fire cause should be made only after: (915)
    A. a suspect has been named in the case.
    B. all overhaul operations are completed.
    C. the state fire marshal's office has been briefed on the incident.
    D. the investigator and ranking fire officer have agreed to its accuracy and validity.

21. Which of the following statements about hearsay is MOST accurate? (916)
    A. It should be ignored.
    B. It should be treated as fact.
    C. It should be rephrased to sound more factual.
    D. It should be reported to the investigator for validation.

22. Which of the following statements about overhaul operations is MOST accurate? (916)
    A. Properly done overhaul operations should leave no traces of fire cause.
    B. Overhaul operations cannot have an effect on the fire cause investigation.
    C. Overhaul operations should be started simultaneously with salvage operations.
    D. Improperly done overhaul operations can be detrimental to the fire cause investigation.

23. Why is having a written account of observations during an incident important? (916)
    A. It is required under NIMS-ICS.
    B. Firefighters may have to testify in court.
    C. It is required to file worker's compensation claims.
    D. It prevents the fire department from having negative publicity.

24. When should overhaul operations begin? (916)
    A. As soon as personnel and equipment are available
    B. After the origin and cause of the fire have been determined
    C. Overhaul operations can be started simultaneously with fire attack.
    D. Overhaul operations can be started simultaneously with salvage operations.

25. The fire department has the authority to deny access to a building: (916)
    A. at their discretion for any length of time.
    B. only when the police have approved the request.
    C. only during fire fighting operations until the fire is considered extinguished.
    D. during fire fighting operations and for a reasonable length of time after fire suppression is terminated.

26. To reenter the premises once all fire personnel have left the scene: (916)
    A. nothing is required.
    B. police escort is required.
    C. a search warrant is required.
    D. a statement of purpose is required.

27. What is needed for an individual who is not a fire department employee to enter the fire scene? (916)
    A. Media pass
    B. Driver's license
    C. Fire investigator's permission
    D. Permission from any firefighter

28. The legal precedent for firefighters being required to have a search warrant to reenter the scene once they have left is based on: (917)
    A. state privacy laws.
    B. the Fifth Amendment.
    C. a decision by the federal appeals court.
    D. a decision by the U.S. Supreme Court.

29. How many individuals should the fire department leave on the premises until an investigator arrives if there is incendiary evidence? (917)
    A. At least one person should remain on the premises
    B. At least two people should remain on the premises
    C. No one from the fire department needs to remain on the premises.
    D. No individual who fought the fire should leave until the investigator arrives.

Firefighter II

_____ 30. Which of the following statements about protecting and preserving evidence is MOST accurate? (918)

 A. Firefighters should move all evidence into one location.

 B. Firefighters should not take any actions regarding evidence preservation.

 C. Once evidence has been handled by firefighters it is no longer admissible in court.

 D. Firefighters should avoid gathering or handling evidence unless absolutely necessary.

_____ 31. What should be done if partially burned papers are found in a furnace, stove, or fireplace? (918)

 A. They should be placed into a large tub of water.

 B. They should be completely extinguished and shoveled into debris piles.

 C. They should be protected by immediately opening dampers and other openings.

 D. They should be protected by immediately closing dampers and other openings.

_____ 32. Which of the following is the BEST way to preserve human footprints? (918)

 A. Place webbing over them

 B. Place caution tape around them

 C. Place a cardboard box over them

 D. Place a salvage cover on top of them

Firefighter II

Fire Department Communications

_____ 1. Which of the following is the generally accepted time period to initiate dispatch? (926)

  A. 1 minute
  B. 3 minutes
  C. 5 minutes
  D. 7 minutes

_____ 2. In most jurisdictions, telecommunicators are: (926)

  A. volunteers.
  B. whomever answers the phone.
  C. part-time off-duty firefighters.
  D. full-time professional communications specialists.

_____ 3. With whom must telecommunicators stay in contact during an incident? (927-928)

  A. Nobody
  B. Initial caller
  C. Incident Commander
  D. Their direct supervisor

_____ 4. Which of the following personnel is generally the first member of the emergency response organization with whom the public has contact during an emergency? (928)

  A. Firefighter
  B. Police officer
  C. Telecommunicator
  D. Incident Commander

_____ 5. What should be done when a nonemergency call comes in over the 9-1-1 system? (928)

  A. The telecommunicator should hang up on the customer.
  B. The customer should be taken care of and his or her request processed.
  C. The customer should be given another number to call and reprimanded for using 9-1-1.
  D. The customer must be transferred to another number to have the service request processed.

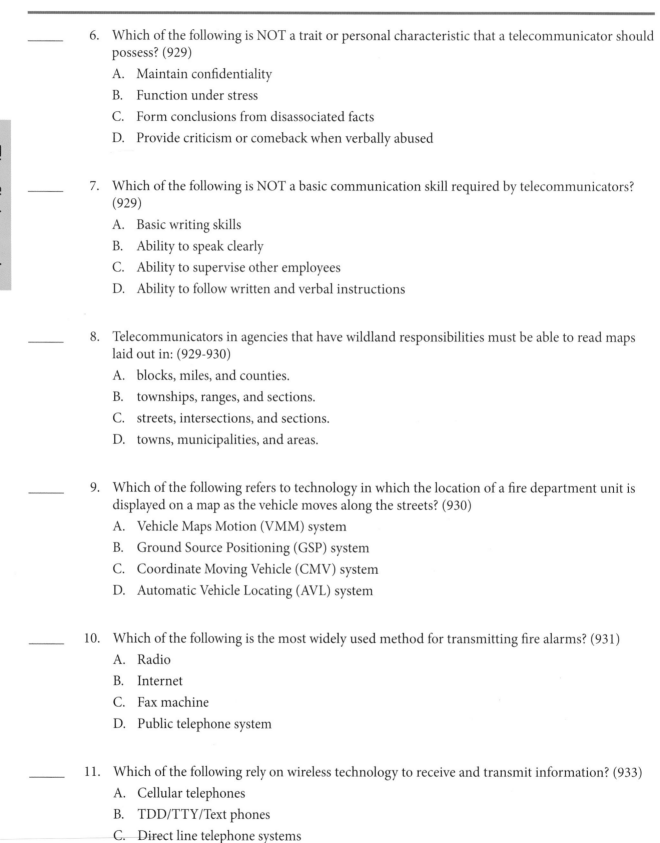

6. Which of the following is NOT a trait or personal characteristic that a telecommunicator should possess? (929)
   A. Maintain confidentiality
   B. Function under stress
   C. Form conclusions from disassociated facts
   D. Provide criticism or comeback when verbally abused

7. Which of the following is NOT a basic communication skill required by telecommunicators? (929)
   A. Basic writing skills
   B. Ability to speak clearly
   C. Ability to supervise other employees
   D. Ability to follow written and verbal instructions

8. Telecommunicators in agencies that have wildland responsibilities must be able to read maps laid out in: (929-930)
   A. blocks, miles, and counties.
   B. townships, ranges, and sections.
   C. streets, intersections, and sections.
   D. towns, municipalities, and areas.

9. Which of the following refers to technology in which the location of a fire department unit is displayed on a map as the vehicle moves along the streets? (930)
   A. Vehicle Maps Motion (VMM) system
   B. Ground Source Positioning (GSP) system
   C. Coordinate Moving Vehicle (CMV) system
   D. Automatic Vehicle Locating (AVL) system

10. Which of the following is the most widely used method for transmitting fire alarms? (931)
    A. Radio
    B. Internet
    C. Fax machine
    D. Public telephone system

11. Which of the following rely on wireless technology to receive and transmit information? (933)
    A. Cellular telephones
    B. TDD/TTY/Text phones
    C. Direct line telephone systems
    D. Commercial phone systems

Firefighter I

12. Which of the following allow the hearing- or speech-impaired community to communicate over the telephone? (932)
    A. Cellular telephones
    B. TDD/TTY/Text phones
    C. Direct line telephone systems
    D. Commercial phone systems

13. Which of the following converts an image, text, or a diagram into digital signals? (933)
    A. Radio
    B. Internet
    C. Fax machine
    D. Public telephone system

14. Which of the following is the primary means by which all elements of the fire department organization communicate with each other? (933)
    A. Radio
    B. Internet
    C. Fax machine
    D. Public telephone system

15. Which of the following statements about computer-aided dispatch (CAD) is MOST accurate? (934)
    A. CAD systems can shorten response times.
    B. CAD systems generally increase response times.
    C. CAD systems cause dispatchers to handle fewer calls.
    D. CAD systems generally increase the amount of radio traffic.

16. Which of the following document emergency telephone calls and can protect the department and its members in case of litigation? (934)
    A. Radio logs
    B. Incident reports
    C. Voice scanners
    D. Voice recorders

17. Which of the following is usually a chronological recording of each and every activity that has been reported or dispatched over the radio? (935)
    A. Radio log
    B. Incident report
    C. Daily activity log
    D. Voice recorder

_____ 18. Which of the following is NOT a basic business telephone courtesy? (936)
- A. Always hang up first.
- B. Answer calls promptly.
- C. Identify the department or company and yourself.
- D. Never leave a caller on hold for an extended period of time.

_____ 19. Which of the following is NOT initial information that should be gathered from an emergency call? (936)
- A. Incident location
- B. Type of incident/situation
- C. Number of people injured or trapped
- D. Number of bystanders watching the incident

_____ 20. Which of the following features of 9-1-1 allows a telecommunicator to maintain access to a caller's phone line? (937)
- A. Ringback
- B. Callback
- C. Forced disconnect
- D. Called party hold

_____ 21. Which of the following features of 9-1-1 allows a telecommunicator to call back a caller's phone after he or she has hung up? (938)
- A. Ringback
- B. Callback
- C. Forced disconnect
- D. Called party hold

_____ 22. Which of the following reports is the MOST likely to come from fire department personnel or other government workers who happen upon an emergency? (938)
- A. Radio
- B. Walk-in
- C. Telephone
- D. Telephone fire alarm box

_____ 23. Which of the following reporting systems is equipped with a telephone for direct voice contact with the telecommunicator? (939)
- A. Wired telegraph circuit box
- B. Telephone fire alarm box
- C. Telegraph fire alarm box
- D. Standard radio fire alarm box

24. Which of the following reporting systems contains an independent radio transmitter with a battery power supply? (939)
   A. Radio fire alarm box
   B. Telegraph fire alarm box
   C. Wired telegraph circuit box
   D. Telephone fire alarm box

25. Which of the following is NOT information the public should give when reporting emergencies? (940)
   A. Their name and location
   B. Nature of the emergency
   C. How many times they have called 9-1-1
   D. Telephone number from which they are calling

26. Which of the following statements about alerting fire department personnel is MOST accurate? (941-942)
   A. Staffed and unstaffed stations are alerted in the same manner.
   B. Alerting unstaffed stations is a time-consuming, long process.
   C. Pagers and cellular phones are used to alert unstaffed station personnel.
   D. All dispatch incident information must be given before emergency vehicles are en route.

27. In the United States, all radio communication is under the authority of the: (943)
   A. Federal Trade Commission (FTC).
   B. Federal Communications Commission (FCC).
   C. Consumer Product Safety Commission (CPSC).
   D. Occupational Safety and Health Administration (OSHA).

28. Which of the following is used for radio communications, especially in the wildland fire community? (943)
   A. Ten-code
   B. Clear text
   C. Fire jargon
   D. Plain English

29. Which of the following is a guideline for radio communication? (943-944)
   A. Be concise and to the point.
   B. Use a monotone speaking voice.
   C. Use slang or regional expressions.
   D. Speak as quickly as possible to save time.

_____ 30. When transmitting information and orders via radio, what information should be transmitted? (944)
   A. Only essential information
   B. As much detail as possible
   C. Sender's opinion of the incident
   D. Only information verified by the Incident Commander

_____ 31. How far should you hold the radio/microphone from your mouth when transmitting? (945)
   A. As close as possible to your mouth
   B. 1 to 2 inches (25 mm to 50 mm) from your mouth
   C. 2 to 4 inches (50 mm to 100 mm) from your mouth
   D. 4 to 6 inches (100 mm to 150 mm) from your mouth

_____ 32. Any unit working at an emergency scene: (945)
   A. has priority over any routine transmissions.
   B. has the same priority as routine transmissions.
   C. has a lesser priority than routine transmissions.
   D. may or may not have priority over routine transmissions.

_____ 33. A situation report provides: (945)
   A. a description of events en route to the incident.
   B. a description of the conditions found when arriving.
   C. a description of conditions after all engines have arrived.
   D. a description of the conditions after the incident is terminated.

_____ 34. Which of the following is the LEAST likely item to be included in a progress report? (946)
   A. Direction of fire spread
   B. Transfer of Command
   C. Any problems or needs
   D. Building and occupancy description

_____ 35. When are tactical channels most often used? (947)
   A. Small routine incidents
   B. Incidents involving any vehicles
   C. Large incidents such as structure fires
   D. Incidents involving fire alarm investigations

36. Which of the following personnel may strike multiple alarms or order additional resources? (947)
    A. Liaison officer
    B. Telecommunicator
    C. Resource section chief
    D. Incident Commander

37. Who is often better equipped to hear weak signals from portable radios that may be distress calls? (948)
    A. Telecommunicators
    B. On-scene personnel
    C. Off-duty personnel
    D. Amateur radio operators

38. When are evacuation signals used? (948)
    A. When the Incident Commander decides that a change in strategy is necessary
    B. When it is time for units operating at an incident to change shifts and go to Rehab
    C. When the Incident Commander wants to confirm the status of all units operating at an incident
    D. When the Incident Commander decides that all firefighters should immediately withdraw from an area

39. Which of the following is a systematic way of confirming the status of any unit operating at an incident? (948)
    A. Staff status log (SSL)
    B. Personnel work log (PWL)
    C. Employee incident report (EIR)
    D. Personnel accountability report (PAR)

40. Which of the following is the LEAST likely reason for a personnel accountability report (PAR) to be requested? (949)
    A. The incident is terminated.
    B. There is a change in strategy.
    C. There is an emergency evacuation.
    D. A firefighter is reported missing or in distress.

Fire Department Communications

_____ 1. Which of the following agencies has the authority over radio communications in the United States? (943)
   A. Federal Aviation Administration (FAA)
   B. Federal Communications Commission (FCC)
   C. Consumer Product Safety Commission (CPSC)
   D. National Institute for Occupational Safety and Health (NIOSH)

_____ 2. The wildland fire community often uses _____ for radio communications. (943)
   A. ten-codes
   B. clear text
   C. plain English
   D. local department codes

_____ 3. Excitement in a telecommunicator's voice can: (943)
   A. make a routine call sound like an emergency.
   B. ensure that the caller understands the seriousness of an event.
   C. increase the likelihood of a rapid response by emergency personnel.
   D. discourage firefighters from calling the telecommunications center.

_____ 4. Which of the following is a guideline for radio communication? (943-944)
   A. Use a moderate rate of speaking.
   B. Over-emphasize important words.
   C. Use slang or regional expressions.
   D. Speak as quickly as possible to save time.

_____ 5. Which of the following is the guiding principle in telecommunications? (944)
   A. Transmit information slowly to ensure accuracy.
   B. Transmit as much information as quickly as possible.
   C. Transmit accurate information as quickly as possible.
   D. Transmit information with as much detail as possible.

Firefighter II

Firefighter II

_____ 6. When transmitting information and orders via radio, what information should be transmitted? (944)

    A. Only essential information

    B. As much detail as possible

    C. Only information verified by the fire chief

    D. Only information verified by the Incident Commander

_____ 7. What should the receiver of a message do after receiving the message? (944)

    A. Acknowledge it by stating "over."

    B. Return to whatever actions they were doing beforehand.

    C. Acknowledge it by stating an affirmation such as "uh huh" or "yes".

    D. Acknowledge it by repeating the essence of the message to the sender.

_____ 8. How far should you hold the radio/microphone from your mouth when transmitting? (945)

    A. As close as possible to your mouth

    B. As far away from your mouth as possible

    C. 1 to 2 inches (25 mm to 50 mm) from your mouth

    D. 2 to 4 inches (50 mm to 100 mm) from your mouth

_____ 9. Which of the following statements about units working at an emergency scene is MOST accurate? (945)

    A. They have priority over any routine transmissions.

    B. They have the same priority as routine transmissions.

    C. They have a lesser priority than routine transmissions.

    D. They may or may not have priority over routine transmissions.

_____ 10. A situation report provides: (945)

    A. a description of events at the fire station when called.

    B. a description of the conditions found when arriving.

    C. a description of conditions after all engines have arrived.

    D. a description of the conditions after the incident is terminated.

_____ 11. Who gives a report on conditions or a situation report? (945)

    A. First company to arrive at the scene of an emergency

    B. Last arriving company at the scene of an emergency

    C. Company at the scene with a communications specialist

    D. Company at the scene that has additional personnel to give the report

_____ 12. Which of the following is the LEAST likely item to be included in a progress report? (946)
   A. Anticipated actions
   B. Transfer of Command
   C. Change in command post location
   D. Building and occupancy description

_____ 13. When are tactical channels most often used? (947)
   A. Small routine incidents
   B. Incidents involving vehicle fires
   C. Large incidents such as structure fires
   D. Incidents involving fire alarm investigations

_____ 14. Who assigns a tactical frequency for the management of the operation or the incident? (947)
   A. Fire chief
   B. Telecommunicator
   C. Incident Commander
   D. Public Information Officer

_____ 15. Who may strike multiple alarms or order additional resources? (947)
   A. Liaison officer
   B. Telecommunicator
   C. Resource section chief
   D. Incident Commander

_____ 16. Who is often better equipped to hear weak signals from portable radios that may be distress calls? (948)
   A. Telecommunicators
   B. On-scene personnel
   C. Off-duty emergency personnel
   D. Amateur ham radio operators

_____ 17. When a request for emergency radio traffic is given, the telecommunicator should: (948)
   A. advise all other units to stand by.
   B. advise all other units to complete their communications.
   C. advise the caller to wait until it is his or her turn to talk.
   D. advise the caller to call back on another radio channel.

Firefighter II

_____ 18. When are evacuation signals used? (948)

    A. When the incident is declared under control

    B. When the Incident Commander decides that the incident is stabilizing

    C. When the Incident Commander wants to confirm the status of all units operating at an incident

    D. When the Incident Commander decides that all firefighters should immediately withdraw from an area

_____ 19. The two most common methods of giving evacuation signals are to broadcast a radio message and: (948)

    A. give hand signals.

    B. yell through a bull horn.

    C. flash lights in a prescribe pattern.

    D. sound audible warning devices on the apparatus.

_____ 20. Which of the following is a systematic way of confirming the status of any unit operating at an incident? (948)

    A. Personnel status log (PSL)

    B. Personnel work log (PWL)

    C. Employee action report (EAR)

    D. Personnel accountability report (PAR)

_____ 21. Which of the following is the LEAST likely reason for a personnel accountability report (PAR) to be requested? (949)

    A. The incident is terminated.

    B. The incident is declared under control.

    C. There is a sudden catastrophic event.

    D. A firefighter is reported missing or in distress.

_____ 22. When can Command request a personnel accountability report (PAR)? (949)

    A. At any time

    B. When given the directive by the fire chief

    C. Only at certain predetermined benchmarks

    D. Only at times when personnel are in jeopardy

_____ 23. Which of the following outlines the necessary information needed to complete incident reports? (949)

    A. National Fire Incident Reporting System (NFIRS)

    B. National Incident Management System (NIMS)

    C. National Fire Safety Incident System (NFSIS)

    D. Occupational Safety and Health Reporting System (OSHR)

_____ 24. Why should reports be filled out in terminology that non-fire service personnel can understand? (949)

    A. Reports are available to the public.

    B. Computer systems don't recognize fire service terminology.

    C. Fire service terminology differs from region to region.

    D. Reports are often completed by administrative personnel.

_____ 25. Which of the following is NOT a purpose of incident reports? (949)

    A. Justify budget requests

    B. Justify resource allocations

    C. Evaluate the needs of the department

    D. Elect department union representatives

Firefighter II

Chapter 20

Fire Prevention and Public Education

_____ 1. What is the purpose of a survey? (961)
   A. To gather or impart information
   B. To present fire and life safety facts to the media
   C. To pass information regarding dangerous activity on to the fire prevention bureau
   D. To ensure compliance with applicable fire and life safety code requirements

_____ 2. What is the purpose of an inspection? (961)
   A. To gather or impart information
   B. To present fire and life safety facts to the media
   C. To familiarize firefighters with the contents of the buildings
   D. To ensure compliance with applicable fire and life safety code requirements

_____ 3. In some jurisdictions, fire inspectors are trained to meet the objectives found in: (962)
   A. NFPA® 1031.
   B. NFPA® 1041.
   C. NFPA® 1982.
   D. NFPA® 1992.

_____ 4. What is a fire hazard? (962)
   A. A condition that decreases the likelihood of a fire starting
   B. A condition that would increase the severity of a fire if one did start
   C. A condition in which two of the four components of the fire tetrahedron is present
   D. A condition in which the heat source is supported by a sufficient fuel supply but has no oxygen

_____ 5. What is the approximate percentage of oxygen present in the air we breathe? (962)
   A. 11
   B. 21
   C. 31
   D. 41

_____ 6. What is the most manageable of the combustion components? (962)
   A. Fuel supply
   B. Heat source
   C. Oxygen supply
   D. Self-sustained chemical reaction

Firefighter II

_____ 7. Which of the following heat source hazards results from an oxidizer and reducing agent coming into contact with and reacting to each other? (963)
   A. Nuclear heat energy
   B. Chemical heat energy
   C. Electrical heat energy
   D. Mechanical heat energy

_____ 8. Which of the following heat source hazards results from heat that is created by fission? (963)
   A. Nuclear heat energy
   B. Chemical heat energy
   C. Electrical heat energy
   D. Mechanical heat energy

_____ 9. Which of the following heat source hazards results from exposed wiring? (963)
   A. Nuclear heat energy
   B. Chemical heat energy
   C. Electrical heat energy
   D. Mechanical heat energy

_____ 10. Which of the following heat source hazards results from moving parts on machines, such as belts and bearings? (963)
   A. Nuclear heat energy
   B. Chemical heat energy
   C. Electrical heat energy
   D. Mechanical heat energy

_____ 11. Which of the following is a hazard caused by the unsafe acts of individuals? (964)
   A. Ideal fire hazard
   B. Special fire hazard
   C. Personal fire hazard
   D. Exclusive fire hazard

_____ 12. Which of the following hazards is one that arises as a result of the processes or operations that are characteristics of the individual occupancy? (964)
   A. Target fire hazard
   B. Special fire hazard
   C. Personal fire hazard
   D. Common fire hazard

13. Which of the following would MOST likely be a special hazard of a manufacturing occupancy? (965)
    A. Illegal storage
    B. Inadequate fire extinguishers
    C. Storage aisles incorrect distance apart
    D. Large-scale use of flammable and combustible gases

14. Which of the following would MOST likely be a special hazard of public assembly occupancies? (965)
    A. Materials stored in paths of egress
    B. Operation of vehicles inside buildings
    C. Existence of open voids in multiple occupancies
    D. Storage of large quantities of combustible products

15. A structure in which there is a greater-than-normal potential for the loss of life or property form a fire is known as a: (966)
    A. target hazard.
    B. special hazard.
    C. personal hazard.
    D. common hazard.

16. Which of the following is MOST likely to be identified as a target hazard occupancy? (966)
    A. A parked car
    B. A lumberyard
    C. An empty playground
    D. A single-family residence

17. What should firefighters do if they are unsure about the answer to a property owner's technical question? (966)
    A. They should recommend that the property owner research the subject.
    B. They should research the question and convey the answer to the property owner.
    C. They should give the most convincing answer they can produce at that moment.
    D. They should minimize the property owner's concerns in order to finish the inspection in a timely manner.

18. Which of the statements about firefighters who conduct inspections is MOST accurate? (967)
    A. They should present a well-groomed, neat appearance.
    B. They should know all the answers to technical questions.
    C. They should wear their cleanest, most comfortable clothing.
    D. They should limit research prior to conducting an inspection.

Firefighter II

_____ 19. Which of the following is MOST likely to be needed for conducting an inspection? (967)
   A. Full PPE
   B. A flashlight
   C   Forcible entry tools
   D. A thermal imaging camera

_____ 20. In most cases, when should fire inspections be conducted? (968)
   A. When the owner is absent
   B. After normal business hours
   C. During normal business hours
   D. When customers are not present

_____ 21. Which of the following statements about conducting fire inspections is MOST accurate? (968-970)
   A. The occupant should NOT accompany the inspection team.
   B. The inspection team should NOT ask to inspect locked rooms.
   C. The inspection team should make a note of the cleanliness of the facility.
   D. The team should enter the premises at the back entrance to avoid blocking customers.

_____ 22. What must be done if one or more code violations are found? (969-970)
   A. A plan of correction must be agreed upon.
   B. A release of liability must be signed by the owner.
   C. The property owner should be fined for each violation.
   D. The facility should be shut down until violations are corrected.

_____ 23. What is the specific purpose of a preincident planning survey? (970)
   A. To gather information
   B. To impart information
   C. To report and cite code violations
   D. To gauge the occupants' fire knowledge

_____ 24. What is the specific purpose of a residential fire safety survey? (970)
   A. To gather information
   B. To impart information
   C. To report and cite code violations
   D. To gauge the occupants' fire knowledge

_____ 25. Which of the following statements about residential fire safety surveys is MOST accurate? (970)

    A. Occupant participation is voluntary.

    B. Occupant participation is mandatory.

    C. They are offered for a small fee to cover costs.

    D. They are used to enforce local fire codes.

_____ 26. The bulk of fuel available to burn is known as the: (971)

    A. fuel load.

    B. burn base.

    C. fire hazard.

    D. flammable content.

_____ 27. The distance from the street line to the front of a building is known as the: (972)

    A. curb.

    B. setback.

    C. entrance.

    D. sidewalk.

_____ 28. Which of the following survey methods do many firefighters find LEAST confusing when conducting an interior survey? (972)

    A. Start on the roof and work downward.

    B. Start on the ground floor and work from side to side.

    C. Position one firefighter on each level of the building to work independently.

    D. Start in the basement, then proceed to the floor most likely to pose the greatest danger.

_____ 29. What should firefighters do when floor plan drawings are not available from the building owner? (972)

    A. Create floor plan drawings.

    B. Operate without floor plan drawings.

    C. Demand floor plan drawings from the owner.

    D. Take photographs to use in place of floor plan drawings.

_____ 30. Which of the following statements about conducting preincident planning surveys is MOST accurate? (972)

    A. The survey should begin inside the building.

    B. All buildings on the property should be surveyed separately.

    C. Survey results should not be discussed with the owner or occupant.

    D. Regardless of the size of the building, only one visit should be made.

Firefighter II

_____ 31. Which of the following provides important detail and quickly records a tremendous amount of information especially if taken from more than one angle? (975-976)

    A. A map

    B. A sketch

    C. A photograph

    D. A scale floor plan

_____ 32. Where do most civilian fire casualties occur in the U.S. each year? (976)

    A. Vehicles

    B. Residences

    C. Storage facilities

    D. Commercial businesses

_____ 33. Which of the following statements about residential fire safety surveys is MOST accurate? (976)

    A. Surveys of individual apartment units are mandatory.

    B. Surveys of other-than-common areas of a hotel are always mandatory.

    C. Residential fire safety surveys are code enforcement activities.

    D. Residential fire safety surveys of single-family dwellings are voluntary.

_____ 34. Which of the following is NOT a main objective of a residential fire safety survey? (976)

    A. Preventing accidental fires

    B. Improving life safety conditions

    C. Citing owners for code violations

    D. Helping the owner understand existing conditions

_____ 35. What is the primary reason for conducting residential fire safety surveys? (977)

    A. To become better acquainted with home construction

    B. To reduce hazards associated with loss of life or property

    C. To discuss fire and life safety information with the occupant

    D. To promote positive public relations and community support

_____ 36. Which of the following is a guideline for conducting residential fire safety surveys? (978)

    A. Cite owners/occupants for code violations.

    B. Compliment the occupants for favorable conditions.

    C. Share survey results with neighbors to increase their awareness.

    D. Survey all livable rooms; garages and storage rooms are exempt.

Firefighter II

_____ 37. Which of the following is a common cause of residential fires? (978)

    A. Obstructed sprinklers

    B. Exposed electrical wiring

    C. Highly combustible interior finishes

    D. High-piled storage of combustible materials

_____ 38. When should firefighters recommend occupants change the battery in their battery-operated smoke alarms? (980)

    A. Monthly

    B. Biannually

    C. When clocks are reset due to Daylight Savings Time

    D. When the old battery wears out and the unit no longer works

_____ 39. Where small children reside, the recommended water temperature setting is: (980)

    A. at least 110°F (43°C).

    B. at least 130°F (54°C).

    C. no higher than 100°F (38°C).

    D. no higher than 120°F (49°C).

_____ 40. When conducting an exterior survey of a residence, firefighters should note whether dry vegetation exists within how many feet of the house? (980)

    A. 30 feet (10 m)

    B. 40 feet (12 m)

    C. 50 feet (15 m)

    D. 60 feet (18 m)

_____ 41. Gasoline, propane, and other flammable liquids and gases should: (980)

    A. never be brought into a dwelling.

    B. never be brought into a dwelling unless proper ventilation exists.

    C. be brought into a dwelling only if kept in separate containers.

    D. be brought into a dwelling when being used for cleaning purposes.

_____ 42. Which of the following statements regarding home safety recommendations is MOST accurate? (982)

    A. Keep at least three exits available for escape if a fire starts.

    B. Only leave infants alone in the bathtub for a minimal amount of time.

    C. Turn pans full of hot liquids so their handles are accessible to small children.

    D. Maintain a clear and unobstructed exit pathway for escape if a fire starts.

_____ 43. The *Four E's* of effective injury prevention are education, engineering, enforcement, and: (982)

A. elapse.

B. elevation.

C. effective response.

D. economic incentive.

_____ 44. Which of the following statements about fire and life safety messages is MOST accurate? (982)

A. They cannot contain statistics.

B. They have to focus on fire safety only.

C. They should not be created by firefighters.

D. They must be targeted to the specific audience.

_____ 45. A general consideration of fire and life safety messages is: (982)

A. brevity.

B. accuracy.

C. including negativity to create impact.

D. targeting a broad audience to be most effective.

_____ 46. Which of the following messages would be the BEST for a firefighter to use? (983)

A. Get out! Get out!

B. Stand up in smoke.

C. Do not call the operator!

D. Do not hide in the closet.

_____ 47. Which of the following is the first step of the basic four-step method of instruction? (984-986)

A. Evaluation

B. Preparation

C. Application

D. Presentation

_____ 48. Which step of the basic four-step method of instruction involves assessing the effectiveness of the fire and life safety program? (984-986)

A. Evaluation

B. Preparation

C. Application

D. Presentation

49. What happens during the application step of the basic four-step method of instruction? (984-986)
   A. Facts and ideas are presented to the audience.
   B. The presenter learns the message that will be delivered.
   C. Educational gain is measured and used to modify the program for future use.
   D. Participants are given the opportunity to use information they have been presented.

50. Which step of the basic four-step method of instruction involves explaining information, using visual aids, and demonstrating techniques? (984-986)
   A. Evaluation
   B. Preparation
   C. Application
   D. Presentation

51. The internal process in which energy is expended in the direction of goals is known as: (985)
   A. learning.
   B. teaching.
   C. education.
   D. motivation.

52. Which of the following time spans would be BEST when presenting to young children? (986)
   A. 15 minutes
   B. 30 minutes
   C. 45 minutes
   D. 1 hour

53. Which of the following is a guideline for presenting fire and life safety information to young children? (986-987)
   A. Children learn by listening, not by doing.
   B. Do NOT ask a misbehaving child for help.
   C. Scare children if necessary to make your point.
   D. Get down to the children's eye level to build rapport.

54. What do firefighters recommend that individuals do if their clothing catches on fire? (988)
   A. Run.
   B. Beat the fire.
   C. Look for water.
   D. Stop, drop, and roll.

Firefighter II

_____ 55. Which of the following rules should be communicated to residential occupants? (988)

    A. Stay standing to avoid heated gases.

    B. Have two emergency exits from every room.

    C. Keep bedroom doors open during sleeping hours.

    D. Call the fire department before leaving the structure.

_____ 56. Which of the following statements about candle use is MOST accurate? (988-990)

    A. Keep candles away from pets.

    B. Move lighted candles carefully.

    C. Use candles during power outages for maximum safety.

    D. Leave lighted candles unattended for short periods of time.

_____ 57. Which of the following is usually the feasible recommendation for placement of smoke alarms? (990)

    A. One in every room

    B. One every 10 feet (3 m)

    C. One in every bedroom and one at every level of the living unit

    D. One in the kitchen, one in the garage, and one in the master bedroom

_____ 58. Which of the following statements about carbon monoxide detectors is MOST accurate? (991)

    A. They are unnecessary for most residences.

    B. They cannot be used interchangeably with smoke alarms.

    C. They should not be installed in the same locations as smoke alarms.

    D. Their maintenance requirements are different than those for smoke alarms.

_____ 59. Which of the following statements about fire station tours is MOST accurate? (992)

    A. Visitors should be allowed to pet any station mascot.

    B. Visitors should not see negative activities while at the station.

    C. Visitors should be allowed to try on fire helmets and other gear.

    D. Visitors should be given the opportunity to roam the station alone.

_____ 60. Which of the following is one of the first things to do when visitors are in the fire station? (992)

    A. Provide refreshments for visitors.

    B. Provide information packets for visitors.

    C. Provide safety instructions about what to do if an alarm sounds.

    D. Provide visitors with envelopes in which they can put a donation.

Chapter 21

Basic Prehospital Emergency Medical Care for Firefighters

_____ 1. The organisms that cause infection are called: (1004)
   A. viruses.
   B. bacteria.
   C. pathogens.
   D. antibodies.

_____ 2. Which of the following is a requirement of employees regarding BSI? (1004)
   A. Employees must pay for immunizations.
   B. Employees must follow the exposure control plan.
   C. Employees must develop a written exposure control plan.
   D. Employees must provide their own personal protective equipment.

_____ 3. Which of the following type of gloves should be used to clean the ambulance and soiled equipment? (1005)
   A. Latex
   B. Vinyl
   C. Leather
   D. Heavyweight, tear-resistant

_____ 4. Which of the following should be worn when tuberculosis is suspected? (1006)
   A. Surgical mask
   B. Supplied-air respirator
   C. NIOSH-approved self-contained breathing apparatus
   D. NIOSH-approved N-95 or high efficiency particulate air respirator

_____ 5. Which disease of concern sometimes settles in the lungs and can be fatal? (1008)
   A. SARS
   B. AIDS
   C. West Nile
   D. Tuberculosis

_____ 6. Which disease of concern is spread by mosquitoes? (1009)
   A. SARS
   B. Hepatitis
   C. West Nile
   D. Tuberculosis

_____ 7. Which type of hepatitis is acquired through blood exposure and has no vaccination? (1007-1008)

A. Hepatitis A

B. Hepatitis B

C. Hepatitis C

D. Hepatitis Delta

_____ 8. Which disease of concern is a set of conditions that result when the immune system has been attacked by HIV (human immunodeficiency virus)? (1008)

A. SARS

B. AIDS

C. West Nile

D. Tuberculosis

_____ 9. Which federal regulation mandates measures that employers of emergency responders must take to protect employees who are likely to be exposed to blood and other body fluids? (1009)

A. Ryan White CARE Act

B. Hepatitis Exposure Requirement

C. Tuberculosis Compliance Mandate

D. Bloodborne Pathogens Standard

_____ 10. Which law describes the selection and proper use of different kinds of respirators? (1013)

A. Ryan White CARE Act

B. Hepatitis Exposure Requirement

C. Tuberculosis Compliance Mandate

D. Bloodborne Pathogens Standard

_____ 11. Which law mandates a procedure by which emergency response personnel find out if they have been exposed to potentially life-threatening diseases while providing patient care? (1010-1011)

A. Ryan White CARE Act

B. Hepatitis Exposure Requirement

C. Tuberculosis Compliance Mandate

D. Bloodborne Pathogens Standard

_____ 12. According to the Bloodborne Pathogens Standard, the Hepatitis B vaccination must be made available: (1010)

A. free of charge.

B. at a discounted rate.

C. only once a year.

D. once every two years.

_____ 13. Which types of personal protective equipment are NOT required to be provided by the employer, according to the Bloodborne Pathogens Standard? (1010)
   A. Protective gloves
   B. Bag-valve masks
   C. Bulletproof vests
   D. Gowns and aprons

_____ 14. Which of the following statements about the Ryan White CARE Act is LEAST accurate? (1010-1013)
   A. It applies to all 50 states.
   B. It defines two notification systems for infectious disease exposure.
   C. It requires a review of a patient's medical records at the request of an emergency worker.
   D. It empowers hospitals to test patients for bloodborne diseases at the request of the emergency worker.

_____ 15. Which of the following is a high-risk area for tuberculosis? (1013)
   A. Walk-in clinics
   B. College campuses
   C. Fire departments
   D. Correctional institutions

_____ 16. Which is the third and final stage of the body's response to stress? (1015)
   A. Exhaustion
   B. Completion
   C. Alarm reaction
   D. Stage of resistance

_____ 17. Which stage of general adaptation syndrome occurs when exposure to a stressor is prolonged or the stressor is particularly severe? (1015)
   A. Exhaustion
   B. Completion
   C. Alarm reaction
   D. Stage of resistance

_____ 18. Which type of stress reaction is also known as post-traumatic stress disorder and can be triggered by a specific incident? (1016)
   A. Acute stress reaction
   B. Delayed stress reaction
   C. Cumulative stress reaction

D. Cataclysmic stress reaction

19. Which of the following is a sign or symptom of acute stress reaction? (1015)

A. It will include flashbacks, nightmares, and/or sleep difficulties.

B. It may not become evident until days, months, or even years later.

C. It develops simultaneously or within a very short time following the incident.

D. It may result in manifestations such as migraines and increased smoking or alcohol intake.

20. Which type of stress reaction is not triggered by a single critical incident, but results from sustained, recurring low-level stressors? (1016)

A. Acute stress reaction

B. Delayed stress reaction

C. Cumulative stress reaction

D. Cataclysmic stress reaction

21. Which of the following is a positive form of stress that helps people work under pressure and respond effectively? (1017)

A. Eustress

B. Distress

C. Primary stress

D. Secondary stress

22. Which of the following is negative and can happen when the stress of a scene becomes overwhelming? (1017-1018)

A. Eustress

B. Distress

C. Primary stress

D. Secondary stress

23. Initial actions should only be taken at hazardous materials incidents if they: (1019)

A. stop the leak completely.

B. protect responders, patients, and bystanders.

C. are performed while wearing a self-contained breathing apparatus.

D. are supervised by an appropriately trained hazardous materials team.

24. When responding to scenes involving dangerous or violent situations, the action of taking cover and concealing yourself is: (1021)

A. planning.

B. observing

C. reacting.

D. evaluating.

_____ 25. If it is necessary to retreat, place at least ___ major obstacles between yourself and the danger. (1021)
A. one
B. two
C. three
D. four

_____ 26. If ___ are found, stop what you are doing and radio police immediately. (1022)
A. pets
B. valuables
C. small children
D. weapons or drugs

_____ 27. Which of the following do NOT protect the heart? (1023)
A. Ribs
B. Sternum
C. Kidneys
D. Spinal column

_____ 28. The heart contains ___ chambers. (1023)
A. two
B. three
C. four
D. five

_____ 29. In the lungs, blood picks up incoming oxygen and releases ___ for exhalation. (1023)
A. oxygen
B. carbon dioxide
C. carbon monoxide
D. deoxygenated blood

_____ 30. Which of the following is NOT a site for easily feeling the pulse? (1024)
A. Radial artery
B. Carotid artery
C. Brachial artery
D. Pulmonary artery

_____ 31. The _____ pulse can be felt in the neck. (1024)
    A. carotid
    B. radial
    C. brachial
    D. femoral

_____ 32. After ___ minutes without a pulse, irreversible damage occurs to the brain. (1024)
    A. 1 to 2
    B. 2 to 4
    C. 4 to 6
    D. 8 to 10

_____ 33. After assessing the adult patient, what should be done next? (1025-1027)
    A. Activate EMS.
    B. Open the airway.
    C. Position the patient.
    D. Perform rescue breathing.

_____ 34. Make sure that the patient is lying on their ___ before attempting to open the airway. (1027)
    A. back
    B. stomach
    C. left side
    D. right side

_____ 35. Most airway problems are caused by the: (1027)
    A. lips.
    B. teeth.
    C. mouth.
    D. tongue.

_____ 36. What should you do if a second ventilation is unsuccessful? (1029)
    A. Reposition the patient's head.
    B. Continue to perform rescue breathing.
    C. Perform airway clearance techniques.
    D. Begin chest compressions with ventilations.

_____ 37. If an infant or child has a pulse slower than ___ beats per minute, begin CPR. (1031)
    A. 60
    B. 70
    C. 80
    D. 100

Firefighter I

_____ 38. When providing chest compressions, the sternum of a typical adult should be depressed about ___ inches. (1032)

   A. 1 to 1½
   B. 1½ to 2
   C. 2 to 4
   D. 3½ to 5

_____ 39. When performing rescue breathing for an adult, the ventilation rate is: (1030)

   A. 6-8 breaths/minute.
   B. 8-10 breaths/minute.
   C. 10-12 breaths/minute.
   D. 12-14 breaths/minute.

_____ 40. What is the compression depth for an infant patient? (1036)

   A. ⅓ to ½ depth of chest
   B. ½ to ¾ depth of chest
   C. 1½ to 2 inches
   D. 2 to 4 inches

_____ 41. Where is the pulse check location for an infant? (1035)

   A. Radial artery
   B. Brachial artery
   C. Carotid artery
   D. Femoral artery

_____ 42. How long is each ventilation on a child patient? (1036)

   A. 1 second
   B. 2 seconds
   C. 3 seconds
   D. 4 seconds

_____ 43. When working alone on an adult patient, call 9-1-1 after: (1034)

   A. 2 minutes of resuscitation.
   B. 5 minutes of resuscitation.
   C. determining pulselessness.
   D. determining unresponsiveness.

_____ 44. Which of the following is a red or purple skin discoloration that indicates that the patient has been dead for more than 15 minutes? (1037)

A. Rigor mortis

B. Decapitation

C. Line of lividity

D. Decomposition

_____ 45. Which procedure should be used for an obese patient with an airway obstruction? (1038)

A. Chest thrusts

B. Perform CPR

C. Abdominal thrusts

D. Series of 5 back blows and 5 chest thrusts

_____ 46. When clearing an airway obstruction for an unconscious infant the first step is to: (1039)

A. perform CPR.

B. open airway.

C. attempt to ventilate.

D. establish unresponsiveness.

_____ 47. Which component of the circulatory system carries oxygen-rich blood away from the heart? (1041)

A. Lung

B. Vein

C. Artery

D. Capillary

_____ 48. Which component of the circulatory system carries blood to the heart? (1041)

A. Vein

B. Lung

C. Artery

D. Capillary

_____ 49. Which type of bleeding is dark red or maroon? (1042)

A. Arterial bleeding

B. Venous bleeding

C. Capillary bleeding

D. Pulmonary bleeding

_____ 50. Which type of bleeding is often rapid and profuse? (1042)
   A. Arterial bleeding
   B. Venous bleeding
   C. Capillary bleeding
   D. Pulmonary bleeding

_____ 51. Which type of bleeding is slow and "oozing" and is considered minor and easily controlled? (1043)
   A. Arterial bleeding
   B. Venous bleeding
   C. Capillary bleeding
   D. Pulmonary bleeding

_____ 52. Elevation of the extremity should be used in conjunction with ___ for best results to control external bleeding. (1045)
   A. CPR
   B. direct pressure
   C. pressure points
   D. prompt transport

_____ 53. For bleeding from an upper extremity, apply pressure to a point over the ___ artery. (1045-1046)
   A. radial
   B. carotid
   C. femoral
   D. brachial

_____ 54. If trained to do so, administer ___ to the patient with internal bleeding. (1050)
   A. IV antibiotics
   B. nitrous oxide
   C. low-concentration oxygen
   D. high-concentration oxygen

_____ 55. Which type of shock may be caused by sepsis or an anaphylactic reaction? (1051)
   A. Shock
   B. Cardiogenic shock
   C. Hypovolemic shock
   D. Neurogenic/vasodilatory shock

_____ 56. Which type of shock may be suffered by patients suffering a heart attack? (1051)
- A. Shock
- B. Cardiogenic shock
- C. Hypovolemic shock
- D. Neurogenic/vasodilatory shock

_____ 57. Which type of shock may be caused by a slow, fast, or irregular heartbeat? (1051)
- A. Shock
- B. Cardiogenic shock
- C. Hypovolemic shock
- D. Neurogenic/vasodilatory shock

_____ 58. Which sign of shock may include anxiety, restlessness, and combativeness? (1052)
- A. Vital sign changes
- B. Nausea and vomiting
- C. Altered mental status
- D. Pale, cool, clammy skin

_____ 59. Which of the following is NOT a step in the emergency care of shock? (1053)
- A. Control any external bleeding.
- B. Maintain an open airway.
- C. Transport the patient immediately.
- D. Cool the patient with wet towels.

_____ 60. The goal for on-scene time when caring for a trauma or shock patient is a maximum of: (1053)
- A. 5 minutes.
- B. 10 minutes.
- C. 15 minutes.
- D. 20 minutes.

Chapter 22

Introduction to Hazardous Materials

Firefighter I

_____ 1. Any material that possesses an unreasonable risk to the health and safety of persons and/or the environment if it is not properly controlled during handling is known as a: (1059)

    A. CBRNE material.

    B. chemical product.

    C. hazardous material.

    D. controlled dangerous substance.

_____ 2. Hazardous materials are called by the following name in Canadian and U.N. regulations: (1059)

    A. dangerous goods.

    B. E.P.A. regulated items.

    C. U.N. international hazards.

    D. controlled dangerous substances.

_____ 3. The lowest level of training established by NFPA® for first responders at hazardous materials incidents is: (1060)

    A. Specialist Level.

    B. Awareness Level.

    C. Technician Level.

    D. Operations Level.

_____ 4. Which of the following definitions best describes the operations level of hazardous materials training? (1060)

    A. The lowest level of training established by the NFPA® for any first responder at hazardous materials incidents

    B. The highest level of training established by the NFPA® for responders at hazardous materials incidents

    C. The level of training established by the NFPA® allowing responders to implement and take offensive actions at haz mat incidents.

    D. The level of training established by the NFPA® allowing first responders to take defensive actions at hazardous materials incidents

_____ 5. The commonly used manual that aids emergency response personnel in identifying hazardous materials placards is known as: (1061)

    A. _Signs and Symbols of Hazards._

    B. _Emergency Response Guidebook._

    C. _Manual of Common Emergencies._

    D. _Safe Handling of Hazardous Materials._

6. Which of the following entities must certify SCBA for use at hazardous materials incidents? (1062)

A. Environmental Protection Agency (EPA)

B. Occupational Safety and Health Administration (OSHA)

C. National Institute for Occupational Safety and Health (NIOSH) and Mine Safety and Health Administration (MSHA)

D. American National Standards Institute (ANSI) and United States Army Soldier and Biological Chemical Command (SBCCOM)

7. Which of the following types of SCBA is allowed in hazardous materials incidents? (1062)

A. Demand open-circuit

B. Demand closed-circuit

C. Positive-pressure open circuit

D. Pressure-demand closed circuit

8. Where on an SCBA should a responder look to verify compliance with Chemical, Biological, Radiological, and Nuclear agents (CBRN) criteria? (1063)

A. Cylinder

B. Backplate

C. Facepiece

D. Air-supply hose

9. Which of the following is an advantage of a supplied air respirator (SAR) over SCBA? (1064)

A. Reduced weight

B. Reduced airline restriction

C. Reduced potential for heat damage

D. Reduced potential for mechanical damage

10. Which of the following statements about air-purifying respirators (APRs) is MOST accurate? (1064)

A. They supply air from a separate source.

B. They may be powered or non-powered.

C. They protect against all chemical hazards.

D. They are only available with full facepieces.

11. The common name for a granular, porous filtering material used in vapor- or gas-removing respirators is: (1067)

A. soot.

B. sorbent.

C. lixiviator.

D. permeator.

12. Powered air-purifying respirators (PAPRs) should only be used in situations where: (1067)
    A. at least 13.5 percent oxygen is present.
    B. at least 15.5 percent oxygen is present.
    C. at least 17.5 percent oxygen is present.
    D. at least 19.5 percent oxygen is present.

13. Which of the following statements about escape respirators is MOST accurate? (1068)
    A. They are not self-contained.
    B. They are designed for escaping the hot zone.
    C. They cannot accommodate glasses and facial hair.
    D. They are designed for 30-45 minutes of protection.

14. Which of the following is a limitation of respiratory equipment? (1068)
    A. Facepieces hinder voice communication.
    B. APRs can only be worn in IDLH atmospheres.
    C. APRs can only be worn in oxygen-deficient atmospheres.
    D. Only one type of cartridge is available for use with all chemicals.

15. Which of the following statements about structural fire fighting protective clothing is MOST accurate? (1069-1070)
    A. Structural fire fighting clothing is corrosive-resistant.
    B. Hazardous materials cannot remain in the protective equipment.
    C. Rubber in boots and SCBA facepieces can become permeated by chemicals and rendered unsafe for use.
    D. Structural fire fighting protective equipment should only be used when contact with splashes of haz mat materials is likely.

16. Which of the following statements about high-temperature protective clothing is MOST accurate? (1070-1071)
    A. High-temperature protective clothing limits the wearer's vision and mobility.
    B. Proximity suits provide less heat protection than standard structural fire fighting protective clothing.
    C. Fire-entry suits provide close-proximity protection at radiant heat temperatures as high as 3,000°F (1,649°C).
    D. High-temperature protective clothing is designed to protect the wearer from long-term high-temperature exposures.

_____ 17. Which of the following statements about chemical-protective clothing is MOST accurate? (1071-1072)

    A. Liquid-splash protective clothing can only be encapsulating.

    B. Vapor-protective clothing must be worn with negative-pressure SCBA.

    C. Vapor-protective suits do not allow body heat to escape and can contribute to heat stress.

    D. Chemical-protective clothing is made of a material protects against all types of chemicals.

_____ 18. Which of the following EPA ensembles requires vapor-protective suits? (1074-1078)

    A. Level A

    B. Level B

    C. Level C

    D. Level D

_____ 19. Which of the following is the definition of EPA Level D protection? (1077)

    A. Personal protective equipment that affords the lowest level of respiratory and skin protection

    B. Highest level of skin, respiratory, and eye protection that can be afforded by personal protective equipment

    C. Personal protective equipment that affords a lesser level of respiratory and skin protection than the two higher levels

    D. Personal protective equipment that affords the highest level of respiratory protection, but a lesser level of skin protection

_____ 20. Which of the following EPA ensembles requires full-face or half-mask APRs and hooded chemical-resistant clothing? (1074-1078)

    A. Level A

    B. Level B

    C. Level C

    D. Level D

_____ 21. Which of the following is the definition of EPA Level B protection? (1074-1078)

    A. Personal protective equipment that affords the lowest level of respiratory and skin protection

    B. Highest level of skin, respiratory, and eye protection that can be afforded by personal protective equipment

    C. Personal protective equipment that affords a lesser level of respiratory and skin protection than higher level(s)

    D. Personal protective equipment that affords the highest level of respiratory protection, but a lesser level of skin protection

22. Which of the following NFPA® ensemble classifications is designed to protect responders when the identity of the liquid agent is undetermined? (1079)

A. Class 1

B. Class 2

C. Class 3

D. Class 4

23. Which of the following statements about NFPA® Class 3 ensembles is MOST accurate? (1079)

A. They provide necessary sufficient vapor protection.

B. They are sufficient when victims are not ambulatory.

C. They provide sufficient protection when direct contact with liquid droplets is likely.

D. They are sufficient when the concentration of the vapor is undetermined or in question.

24. Which of the following NFPA® ensemble classifications is designed for use when victims are not ambulatory but are showing signs or symptoms of exposure? (1079)

A. Class 1

B. Class 2

C. Class 3

D. Class 4

25. Which of the following statements about mission-oriented protective posture (MOPP) ensembles is MOST accurate? (1079-1080)

A. They provide three flexible levels of protection.

B. The higher the MOPP level, the lower the protection.

C. The JSLIST ensemble may be worn 120 consecutive days.

D. The JSLIST ensemble provides protection against radioactive particles.

26. Which of the following statements regarding heat-exposure prevention is MOST accurate? (1081-1082)

A. Wearing long cotton undergarments impedes natural body ventilation.

B. Caffeinated drinks before working decreases the chance of dehydration.

C. After a work period in protective clothing, drinking chilled water is best.

D. Balanced diets normally provide enough salts to avoid cramping problems.

27. Which of the following is NOT one of the four environmental conditions that causes cold-related stress? (1082-1083)

A. Dampness

B. Cold water

C. High/cool wind

D. Low elevation

_____ 28. Health effects that are short-term and appear within hours or days are known as: (1084)

    A. acute health effects.

    B. minor health effects.

    C. severe health effects.

    D. chronic health effects.

_____ 29. Health effects that are long-term and may take years to appear are known as: (1084)

    A. acute health effects.

    B. minor health effects.

    C. severe health effects.

    D. chronic health effects.

_____ 30. Hazards that are caused by extreme temperatures are known as: (1084-1085)

    A. thermal hazards.

    B. chemical hazards.

    C. mechanical hazards.

    D. radiological hazards.

_____ 31. Which of the following is the most energetic and hazardous form of radiation? (1085)

    A. Ionizing radiation

    B. Infrared radiation

    C. Microwave radiation

    D. Non-ionizing radiation

_____ 32. Fast-moving, negatively charged electrons emitted from the nucleus during radioactive decay are known as: (1086)

    A. beta particles.

    B. alpha particles.

    C. gamma rays.

    D. neutron radiation.

_____ 33. A packet of electromagnetic energy is known as a(n): (1086)

    A. photon.

    B. neutron.

    C. electron.

    D. gravitron.

34. Ultrahigh energy particles that have a physical mass but no electrical charge are: (1087)

    A. photons.

    B. neutrons.

    C. electrons.

    D. gravitrons.

35. Which of the following is MOST accurate? (1088)

    A. Chronic doses of radiation have no suspected health effects.

    B. Firefighters are likely to encounter lethal doses of radiation at WMD incidents.

    C. Chronic doses of radiation are likely to cause nausea, hair loss, reduced blood count, and fatigue.

    D. Radiation exposures likely to be encountered by firefighters are very unlikely to cause serious health effects.

36. Which of the following statements about radiation protection strategies is MOST accurate? (1085-1086)

    A. The closer to the source, the less the exposure.

    B. Firefighter PPE prevents penetration of alpha and beta radiation.

    C. Lead does NOT prevent penetration of beta radiation.

    D. The shorter the exposure time, the larger the total radiation dose.

37. Substances that affect the oxygenation of the body and generally lead to suffocation are: (1090)

    A. oxidants.

    B. asphyxiants.

    C. smotherants.

    D. antioxidants.

38. The process of taking in materials by breathing through the nose or mouth is: (1091)

    A. contact.

    B. ingestion.

    C. inhalation.

    D. absorption.

39. The process of taking in hazardous materials through the skin or eyes is: (1091)

    A. contact.

    B. ingestion.

    C. inhalation.

    D. absorption.

_____ 40. Which of the following statements about poisons and toxic chemicals is MOST accurate? (1091-1094)

    A. Toxins may have chronic effects.

    B. All toxins have fast-acting, acute effects.

    C. A chemical injury at the site of contact is termed a systemic effect.

    D. Nerve poisons interfere with oxygen flow to the lungs and the blood.

_____ 41. Toxins that cause temporary but sometimes severe inflammation to the eyes, skin, or respiratory system are known as: (1094)

    A. irritants.

    B. corrosives.

    C. convulsants.

    D. carcinogens.

_____ 42. Which of the following is a cancer-causing agent? (1094)

    A. Irritant

    B. Allergen

    C. Convulsant

    D. Carcinogen

_____ 43. The simplest type of microorganism that can only replicate itself in the living cell of its host is a: (1099)

    A. rickettsia.

    B. viral agent.

    C. bacterial agent.

    D. biological toxin.

_____ 44. What is a biological toxin? (1100)

    A. A poison produced by a living organism

    B. A specialized bacteria that lives in arthropod carriers

    C. A microscopic, single-celled organism that causes disease in people

    D. A microorganism that can only replicate itself in the living cell of its host

_____ 45. Which of the following types of hazard causes trauma as a result of direct contact with an object? (1101)

    A. Chemical

    B. Biological

    C. Mechanical

    D. Radiological

_____ 46. Which of the following has neither independent shape nor volume? (1102)

    A. Gas

    B. Mass

    C. Solid

    D. Liquid

_____ 47. The temperature of a substance when the vapor pressure exceeds the atmospheric pressure is the: (1103)

    A. high line.

    B. boiling point.

    C. heat structure.

    D. vaporization level.

_____ 48. What is specific gravity? (1104)

    A. The ability of a liquid to mix with or dissolve in water

    B. The ability of two or more chemicals to react and release energy

    C. The weight of a given volume of pure vapor compared to the weight of an equal volume of dry air

    D. The weight of a substance compared to the weight of an equal volume of water at a given temperature

_____ 49. A chemical's ability to remain in the environment is known as its: (1105)

    A. reactivity.

    B. solubility.

    C. resistence.

    D. persistence.

_____ 50. A breach in which a container suffers a general loss of integrity such as a grenade exploding is a: (1109)

    A. split.

    B. puncture.

    C. disintegration.

    D. runaway crack.

_____ 51. Which of the following statements about hazardous materials identification is MOST accurate? (1114-1117)

    A. Private property is exempt from danger.

    B. Dams are considered potential terrorist targets.

    C. Identifying markings are designed so that destruction during the incident is impossible.

    D. Firefighters always have ample warning of hazardous materials being transported in their jurisdiction.

_____ 52. Into which of the following bulk transportation container categories do box cars fall? (1119)

    A. Cargo tanks

    B. Intermodal containers

    C. Vacuum pressure tanks

    D. Tank and other rail cars

_____ 53. A rigid or flexible portable packaging designed for mechanical handling is a(n): (1132)

    A. ton container.

    B. intermediate bulk container.

    C. pressure container.

    D. bulk-capacity fixed-facility container.

_____ 54. Which of the following types of containers for radioactive materials is used for high-activity materials transported by aircraft? (1133)

    A. Type B

    B. Type C

    C. Excepted

    D. Industrial

_____ 55. Which of the following classifications does the United Nations (UN) system give flammable liquids? (1137)

    A. Class 1

    B. Class 3

    C. Class 5

    D. Class 7

_____ 56. Which of the following statements regarding four-digit United Nations (UN) identification numbers is MOST accurate? (1138)

    A. The number may be preceded by the letters EU.

    B. The number may be placed on a white diamond.

    C. The number may NOT be placed on an orange panel.

    D. The number may NOT be preceded by the letters NA.

_____ 57. The stencil on the exterior of tank cars indicating the standards to which the tank car was built is the: (1156)

    A. capacity stencil.

    B. tank identification.

    C. initials and numbers.

    D. specification marking.

58. The NFPA® 704 standard is designed for use in which of the following situations or hazards? (1159)

   A. Transportation

   B. General public use

   C. Commercial facilities

   D. Chronic health hazards

59. Which of the following statements regarding hazardous materials markings is MOST accurate? (1161-1163)

   A. The EPA regulates the manufacture and labeling of pesticides.

   B. U.S. military markings are required to be placed on military vehicles.

   C. Firefighters will encounter a uniform marking system throughout their jurisdiction.

   D. The term "caution" indicates the product has moderate hazards such as significant health effects.

60. Which of the following statements about written resources is MOST accurate? (1166-1170)

   A. A bill of lading is used by a railroad to indicate origin and destination.

   B. A waybill is used by the trucking industry to indicate route and product.

   C. An MSDS is a form provided by the manufacturer of chemicals containing information about chemical composition.

   D. At transportation incidents, firefighters should be able to use the PCP number to identify materials involved.

61. The orange pages of the *Emergency Response Guidebook* are the: (1176)

   A. ID Number Index.

   B. Material Name Index.

   C. Initial Action Guides.

   D. Table of Initial Isolation.

62. Which of the following is known as the initial isolation zone? (1179)

   A. Structure within which occupants remain in order to provide protection from a rapidly approaching hazard

   B. Circular area within which persons may be exposed to dangerous concentrations upwind of the source

   C. Downwind distance from a hazardous materials incident within which protective actions should be implemented

   D. Distance within which all persons are considered for evacuation in all directions from a hazardous materials incident

_____ 63. Which of the following senses is safest to use in the detection of a hazardous material? (1179)

   A. Vision

   B. Smell

   C. Taste

   D. Touch

_____ 64. Which of the following types of monitoring/detection devices uses light to illuminate a sample, thereby creating a spectral signature that is unique to each material? (1182-1183)

   A. Raman spectroscopy

   B. Ion-mobility spectrometer

   C. Flame ionization detector

   D. Biological immunoassay indicator

_____ 65. How does a photo-ionization detector (PID) operate? (1182-1183)

   A. Uses an ultraviolet lamp to ionize samples of gaseous materials

   B. Utilizes a hydrogen flame to which gaseous materials are exposed

   C. Uses a radioactive source to ionize samples in order to determine their spectra

   D. Utilizes surface acoustical wave technologies to detect nerve agents and toxic materials

_____ 66. A chemical substance that is intended for use in terrorist activities to kill or seriously injure people through its physiological effects is a: (1185)

   A. chemical warfare agent.

   B. radiological material.

   C. biological agent.

   D. chemical massacre toxin.

_____ 67. Which of the following is a biological attack indicator? (1188-1190)

   A. Explosion

   B. Dissemination of unscheduled or unusual spray

   C. Surfaces exhibiting oily droplets and unexplained oily film on water surfaces

   D. Material that is hot or seems to emit heat without any sign of an external heat source

_____ 68. Which of the following is a nuclear attack indicator? (1190)

   A. Presentation of specific unusual diseases

   B. Casualties distributed near ventilation systems

   C. Exceptionally large and/or powerful explosion

   D. Unexpectedly heavy burning or high temperatures

69. Which of the following statements regarding illicit laboratories is MOST accurate? (1191-1201)
    A. Biological labs are unlikely to be equipped with petri dishes.
    B. The presence of fireworks and propane containers may be indicative of an explosives lab.
    C. It is estimated that a significant majority of all illegal clandestine drug labs are set up to produce cocaine.
    D. The recipes for chemical warfare agents are difficult to find, but the ingredients are extremely easy to obtain.

70. Which of the following statements about secondary attacks is MOST accurate? (1201-1202)
    A. Secondary devices are not often hidden or camouflaged.
    B. Secondary devices are usually biological agents of some kind.
    C. Responders should be cautious of containers with unknown liquids or materials.
    D. Responders should thoroughly inspect anything that may conceal an explosive device.

Firefighter I

_____ 1. Which of the following statements regarding haz mat incident priorities is MOST accurate? (1214-1215)

    A. Responders should protect the public first.

    B. Firefighters should seldom use defensive actions.

    C. Environmental protection should be a consideration from the beginning of the mitigation process.

    D. Stabilizing actions should NOT include establishing scene perimeters to prevent the spread of contamination.

_____ 2. In hazardous materials operations, a temporary or permanent barrier that contains or directs the flow of liquids is a: (1215)

    A. dike.

    B. canal.

    C. runoff zone.

    D. containment area.

_____ 3. Which of the following terms is described as causing a hazardous materials incident to become less harsh or hostile? (1215)

    A. Clear

    B. Remedy

    C. Mitigate

    D. Quick fix

_____ 4. Which of the following statements about management structure at a hazardous materials incident is MOST accurate? (1215)

    A. Use of a unified command structure at haz mat incidents is unnecessary.

    B. Firefighters do NOT have to operate in accordance with SOPs and LERPs.

    C. NIMS-ICS should be used at all incidents in the U.S. that involve terrorism.

    D. NIMS-ICS should NOT be used at incidents in the U.S. that involve federal response.

_____ 5. Which of the following steps is usually the FIRST element in haz mat problem solving? (1215)

    A. Plan a response.

    B. Evaluate the process.

    C. Analyze the situation.

    D. Implement the selected response.

6. The initial and ongoing assessment of overall incident conditions is commonly referred to as: (1219)
   A. size-up.
   B. monitoring.
   C. safety check.
   D. incident development.

7. From which of the following directions is it BEST to approach a haz mat incident? (1220)
   A. Upwind, uphill, and upstream
   B. Upwind, uphill, and downstream
   C. Downwind, downhill, and upstream
   D. Downwind, downhill, and downstream

8. What is a Level I haz mat incident? (1221)
   A. One that is the least serious and easiest to handle
   B. One that requires the services of a formal haz mat response team
   C. One that requires resources from state/provincial agencies in addition to unified command
   D. One that is beyond the capabilities of the first response agency/organization having jurisdiction

9. In hazardous materials incidents, a patch to seal a small leak in a container is a: (1222)
   A. dam.
   B. plug.
   C. dike.
   D. hold.

10. Which of the following is the most serious of all hazardous materials incidents? (1221-1224)
    A. Level I
    B. Level II
    C. Level III
    D. Level IV

11. Which of the following types of incidents is beyond the capabilities of the first responders on the scene and requires the services of a formal haz mat team? (1222)
    A. Level I
    B. Level II
    C. Level III
    D. Level IV

_____ 12. Which of the following provides confinement of the hazard to a given area by performing actions such as damming a storm drain? (1225)

    A. Offensive strategy

    B. Defensive strategy

    C. Isolationist strategy

    D. Nonintervention strategy

_____ 13. Which of the following statements about incident action plans is MOST accurate? (1225-1226)

    A. Company officers are exempt from functioning according to the IAP.

    B. Written IAPs are unnecessary for large-scale or complex incidents.

    C. An IAP provides for necessary support resources in addition to strategy.

    D. Written IAPs are always necessary, even for short-term, routine operations.

_____ 14. The process of controlling the flow of a spill and capturing it at some specified location is known as: (1226)

    A. trapping.

    B. mastering.

    C. containment.

    D. confinement.

_____ 15. The act of stopping the further release of a material from its container is known as: (1226)

    A. trapping.

    B. mastering.

    C. containment.

    D. confinement.

_____ 16. Which of the following statements regarding strategic goals and tactical objectives is MOST accurate? (1226-1227)

    A. Strategic goals are uniform at all incidents.

    B. Tactical objectives should not change from one incident to the next.

    C. ICs set the goals based upon the goals of the last hazardous materials incident.

    D. ICs set the goals by using strategies that will achieve successful mitigation of the incident.

_____ 17. What is the isolation perimeter? (1227)

    A. The area surrounding an incident that is potentially very dangerous

    B. The location where accident casualties are held after receiving medical care

    C. The boundary established to prevent access by the public and unauthorized persons

    D. The area away from the emergency scene where units assemble and wait for assignment on the emergency scene

Firefighter I

_____ 18. Which of the following provides for the scene control required at haz mat and terrorist incidents to protect responders from interference by unauthorized persons? (1228)

    A. Staging area

    B. Rehabilitation area

    C. Hazard control zone

    D. Scene assessment zone

_____ 19. The area of an incident that is potentially very dangerous because there are hazardous materials and/or armed and dangerous individuals present is known as the: (1229)

    A. hot zone.

    B. warm zone.

    C. treatment zone.

    D. decontamination zone.

_____ 20. Where does decontamination usually take place? (1229)

    A. Hot zone

    B. Cold zone

    C. Warm zone

    D. Staging zone

_____ 21. In which of the following zones are logistical support functions of a haz mat incident carried out? (1229)

    A. Hot

    B. Cold

    C. Warm

    D. Trauma

_____ 22. The prearranged, temporary strategic location where units assemble and wait until they are assigned to a position on the emergency scene is the: (1229-1230)

    A. hot zone.

    B. warm zone.

    C. staging area.

    D. rehabilitation area.

_____ 23. The location where accident casualties are brought to receive medical assessment before being taken to medical facilities is the: (1230)

    A. warm zone.

    B. staging area.

    C. triage/treatment area.

    D. decontamination zone.

_____ 24. What is the rehabilitation area? (1230)

    A. The area where persons are brought for medical assessment

    B. The area where clothing, people, and equipment are cleaned or secured

    C. The area where emergency personnel can rest, sit or lie down, and have food and drink

    D. The area where personnel and equipment awaiting assignment to the incident are held

_____ 25. Which of the following is described as reciprocal assistance from one fire and emergency services agency to another during an emergency based upon a prearrangement between agencies involved? (1231)

    A. Direct aid

    B. Mutual aid

    C. Automatic aid

    D. Dependent aid

_____ 26. Which of the following is a written agreement between two or more agencies to compulsorily dispatch predetermined resources to any fire reported in the geographic area covered by the agreement? (1231)

    A. Direct aid

    B. Mutual aid

    C. Automatic aid

    D. Dependent aid

_____ 27. Which of the following is the first priority at any incident? (1231)

    A. Decontaminating equipment

    B. Prevention of property damage

    C. Protection and safety of emergency responders

    D. Identifying and containing the hazardous material

_____ 28. What is the minimum number of personnel necessary for performing work in the hot zone? (1233)

    A. 2

    B. 4

    C. 6

    D. 8

_____ 29. Under the Federal Emergency Management Agency (FEMA) Urban Search and Rescue (US&R) Task Force program notification system, what does three short blasts of one second each mean? (1233)

    A. All quiet.

    B. Cease operations.

    C. Evacuate the area.

    D. Resume operations.

30. At complex incidents, which of the following personnel may be appointed to ensure the safety of operations? (1233)
    A. Safety officer
    B. Operations officer
    C. Public information officer
    D. Health and wellness officer

31. To move all people from a threatened area to a safer place is to: (1234-1235)
    A. evacuate.
    B. shelter in place.
    C. decontaminate.
    D. defend in place.

32. Which of the following statements about evacuations is MOST accurate? (1235)
    A. PPE is unnecessary during evacuation.
    B. Responders should evacuate individuals at the edges of the threatened area first.
    C. Knocking on doors is an unacceptable way of notifying residents of an evacuation.
    D. Even after people move the recommended distance, they are not necessarily completely safe.

33. To direct people to go quickly inside a building and remain inside until danger passes is to: (1236)
    A. evacuate.
    B. shelter in place.
    C. decontaminate.
    D. defend in place.

34. Which of the following is considered an offensive role to physically protect those in harm's way? (1237)
    A. Evacuating
    B. Sheltering in place
    C. Defending in place
    D. Educating the public

35. Which of the following statements about decontamination is MOST accurate? (1237-1238)
    A. Decontamination removes all contaminants.
    B. Decontamination procedures are uniform across all organizations.
    C. Emergency responders should be decontaminated separately from victims.
    D. When conducting decontamination of victims, the less clothing removed the better.

36. Using chemical or physical methods to thoroughly remove contaminants from responders is: (1238-1239)
    A. gross decon.
    B. mass decon.
    C. technical decon.
    D. emergency decon.

37. What is the goal of emergency decontamination? (1239)
    A. Protect the environment as much as possible.
    B. Thoroughly protect the environment and the public.
    C. Remove contaminants from as many victims as possible.
    D. Remove the contaminant from the victim as quickly as possible.

38. Which of the following water pressures is recommended as the MINIMUM that should be used in mass decon showers to ensure the process physically removes viscous agent? (1242)
    A. 30 psi (210 kPa)
    B. 40 psi (280 kPa)
    C. 50 psi (350 kPa)
    D. 60 psi (420 kPa)

39. Which of the following victims would be considered ambulatory? (1246)
    A. One who is unconscious
    B. One who walks and talks unassisted
    C. One who cannot understand directions
    D. One who understands directions but cannot move

40. The process in which a hazardous liquid interacts with (or is bound to) the surface of a sorbent material is known as: (1249)
    A. absorption.
    B. adsorption.
    C. neutralization.
    D. chemical degradation.

41. Which of the following is the BEST definition of dilution? (1249)
    A. The process that isolates and disposes of the contaminated item
    B. The process of using water to flush contaminants from contaminated victims
    C. The process that takes a hazardous liquid and treats it chemically so it turns into a solid
    D. The process of using water and a prepared solution to remove contaminants from victims

_____ 42. Which of the following statements regarding site selection for decon implementation is MOST accurate? (1252-1253)

   A. The site must be close to the hazards.

   B. The site needs to be upwind of the hot zone.

   C. The site ideally slopes away from the hot zone.

   D. The site should be as close to storm drains as possible.

_____ 43. Which of the following statements about decon corridor layout is MOST accurate? (1254-1255)

   A. Privacy during decon is an unnecessary concern.

   B. Firefighters working in the decontamination area MUST wear full CPC.

   C. The decontamination corridor may be identified with barrier tape or safety cones.

   D. Responders working in decon do NOT have to pass through decon before leaving the corridor.

_____ 44. Consideration should be given to protecting victims from the cold during decontamination if temperatures are: (1255)

   A. 64°F (18°C) or lower.

   B. 68°F (20°C) or lower.

   C. 72°F (22°C) or lower.

   D. 76°F (24°C) or lower.

_____ 45. Which of the following statements regarding individuals who have been exposed to deadly levels of chemical warfare agents is MOST accurate? (1256)

   A. They should shower while wearing their clothing.

   B. They should disrobe and lightly rinse off their bodies.

   C. They should undergo emergency decon immediately if temperatures permit.

   D. They should be provided with dry clothing and warm shelter as soon as possible after showering.

_____ 46. Which of the following statements about rescue is MOST accurate? (1256-1260)

   A. Rescue is easy to implement.

   B. When necessary, rescue can be conducted without direction of the IC.

   C. Rescue can be performed by available personnel without specialized training.

   D. Operations Level responders may direct contaminated victims to an isolation point.

_____ 47. What is spill control? (1261)

   A. The removal of hazardous materials from victims

   B. The phase in which firefighters rescue contaminated victims

   C. The phase that takes place when the IC determines that all victims have been accounted for

   D. The action that minimizes the amount of contact the product makes with people, property, and the environment

Firefighter I

_____ 48. A physical and/or chemical event occurring during contact between materials that have an attraction for each other is: (1263)

    A. dilution.

    B. absorption.

    C. dissolution.

    D. vapor suppression.

_____ 49. What is one example of blanketing? (1264)

    A. Mechanical control of movement of contaminated air

    B. Construction of curbs that direct the flow of a hazardous material

    C. Application of water to a water-soluble material to reduce the hazard

    D. Use of an appropriate aqueous foam agent to cover the surface of the spill

_____ 50. Which of the following actions is taken to control the flow of liquid hazardous materials away from the point of discharge? (1264)

    A. Diking

    B. Diluting

    C. Vapor dispersion

    D. Blanketing/covering

_____ 51. What is dilution? (1264)

    A. Dissolving a gas in water

    B. Retaining one material in another

    C. Applying water to a water-soluble material

    D. Controlling the movement of air by mechanical means

_____ 52. The process of dissolving a gas in water is called: (1264)

    A. dilution.

    B. retention.

    C. dissolution.

    D. ventilation.

_____ 53. The action taken to direct or influence the course of airborne hazardous materials is known as: (1265)

    A. diking.

    B. damming.

    C. vapor dispersion.

    D. vapor suppression.

_____ 54. What is vapor suppression? (1266)

    A. Directing the course of airborne hazardous materials

    B. Reducing the emission of vapors at a haz mat incident

    C. Controlling the movement of air by mechanical means

    D. Controlling the movement of air by electrical means

_____ 55. Which of the following involves controlling the movement of air by natural means? (1268)

    A. Damming

    B. Ventilating

    C. Dissolving

    D. Suppressing

_____ 56. Which of the following statements about leak control and containment is MOST accurate? (1268-1269)

    A. The goal is to identify the hazardous product.

    B. Offensive actions can be taken by Awareness Level personnel.

    C. It may be safe for Operations-Level responders to operate emergency remote shutoff valves on cargo tank trucks.

    D. Remote shutoff valves that can be operated without entering the hot zone are absent on pipelines carrying hazardous materials.

_____ 57. Which of the following statements about crime scene management and evidence preservation is MOST accurate? (1270)

    A. The framework for a response to a criminal incident is very different from that used for any other type of response.

    B. The Federal Bureau of Investigation (FBI) has jurisdiction over terrorist incidents in the U.S.

    C. The framework for a response to a terrorist incident is very different from that used for any other type of response.

    D. The Occupational Safety and Health Administration (OSHA) has jurisdiction over criminal incidents in the U.S.

_____ 58. The recovery and termination phase of a haz mat incident is also known as the: (1270)

    A. cleanup phase.

    B. mobilization phase.

    C. investigation phase.

    D. demobilization phase.

59. Which of the following statements about decontamination and disposal is MOST accurate? (1272)

    A. All equipment can be decontaminated at the incident site.

    B. Medical waste can be disposed of in regular trash receptacles.

    C. Equipment that is too contaminated to be cleaned can be reused with proper caution.

    D. Hazardous waste must be disposed of in accordance with SOPs and applicable legislation.

60. Which of the following statements about post-incident analysis and critique is MOST accurate? (1273)

    A. It is not advised to use the analysis to evaluate the effectiveness of the response.

    B. The company officer is responsible for assigning someone to write a post-incident report.

    C. The post-incident analysis should take place within two weeks of the incident if possible.

    D. A post-incident analysis should only be scheduled for the main agency involved in the incident.

Firefighter I

Answer Key

Chapter 1

Firefighter I

1. D	13. D	25. A	37. C	49. B
2. D	14. B	26. A	38. C	50. D
3. C	15. C	27. D	39. D	51. C
4. B	16. A	28. D	40. D	52. A
5. C	17. B	29. C	41. D	53. D
6. C	18. C	30. B	42. C	54. A
7. A	19. B	31. A	43. A	55. A
8. C	20. B	32. C	44. B	56. D
9. C	21. A	33. B	45. A	57. A
10. C	22. D	34. D	46. B	58. A
11. C	23. B	35. A	47. A	59. D
12. A	24. C	36. B	48. C	60. A

Chapter 2

Firefighter I

1. C	12. B	23. D	34. B	45. D
2. D	13. D	24. D	35. D	46. B
3. B	14. A	25. D	36. A	47. C
4. C	15. D	26. A	37. B	48. A
5. B	16. C	27. B	38. C	49. D
6. C	17. B	28. D	39. D	50. A
7. C	18. A	29. C	40. A	51. D
8. C	19. C	30. B	41. C	52. A
9. D	20. D	31. A	42. A	53. B
10. A	21. B	32. B	43. D	54. C
11. D	22. A	33. A	44. C	55. D

Chapter 3 Firefighter I

1. A	14. B	27. C	40. C	53. A
2. C	15. A	28. B	41. D	54. B
3. D	16. C	29. A	42. A	55. D
4. C	17. A	30. B	43. A	56. A
5. D	18. A	31. B	44. C	57. D
6. D	19. D	32. C	45. C	58. B
7. C	20. D	33. C	46. D	59. A
8. D	21. C	34. B	47. B	60. A
9. B	22. B	35. B	48. C	61. C
10. B	23. A	36. C	49. D	62. D
11. A	24. A	37. C	50. A	63. B
12. D	25. A	38. B	51. A	
13. B	26. C	39. B	52. B	

Chapter 4 Firefighter I

1. C	12. B	23. C	34. B	45. C
2. A	13. B	24. A	35. C	46. D
3. C	14. D	25. D	36. D	47. B
4. D	15. A	26. A	37. C	48. A
5. B	16. A	27. D	38. D	49. B
6. B	17. C	28. A	39. B	50. D
7. C	18. C	29. D	40. B	51. D
8. D	19. A	30. D	41. D	
9. C	20. A	31. C	42. B	
10. D	21. A	32. A	43. A	
11. A	22. B	33. B	44. B	

Chapter 4 Firefighter II

1. A	9. B	17. B	25. B	33. A
2. B	10. D	18. D	26. C	34. B
3. B	11. C	19. A	27. C	35. C
4. D	12. C	20. C	28. D	36. C
5. C	13. B	21. A	29. C	37. A
6. A	14. A	22. C	30. B	38. B
7. B	15. D	23. C	31. A	39. B
8. B	16. B	24. D	32. B	40. D

Answer Key

1. D	16. D	31. B	46. D	61. D
2. C	17. C	32. A	47. D	62. B
3. D	18. D	33. B	48. B	63. A
4. C	19. D	34. B	49. A	64. C
5. B	20. B	35. A	50. A	65. A
6. B	21. A	36. A	51. D	66. D
7. D	22. B	37. A	52. B	67. B
8. D	23. A	38. D	53. D	68. A
9. A	24. B	39. A	54. B	69. D
10. B	25. B	40. B	55. A	70. A
11. D	26. D	41. B	56. A	71. A
12. A	27. A	42. B	57. B	72. D
13. A	28. B	43. A	58. A	73. B
14. A	29. D	44. D	59. D	74. D
15. D	30. A	45. A	60. B	75. D

1. D	11. C	21. C	31. C	41. A
2. D	12. B	22. B	32. A	42. C
3. A	13. D	23. D	33. C	43. D
4. B	14. B	24. A	34. C	44. B
5. B	15. A	25. A	35. D	45. C
6. C	16. D	26. C	36. B	46. A
7. A	17. C	27. B	37. C	47. C
8. C	18. C	28. B	38. D	48. C
9. C	19. A	29. A	39. B	49. C
10. D	20. B	30. D	40. A	50. A

Answer Key

Chapter 7

1. C	13. C	25. C	37. A	49. A
2. C	14. D	26. A	38. B	50. D
3. D	15. C	27. C	39. D	51. B
4. D	16. A	28. A	40. C	52. A
5. D	17. B	29. D	41. A	53. B
6. D	18. C	30. C	42. B	54. D
7. C	19. C	31. D	43. B	55. A
8. B	20. B	32. A	44. D	56. A
9. C	21. B	33. A	45. A	57. B
10. D	22. B	34. C	46. C	58. C
11. A	23. C	35. B	47. B	
12. B	24. A	36. A	48. A	

Chapter 8

1. B	9. A	17. A	25. B	33. B
2. A	10. C	18. C	26. B	34. C
3. A	11. A	19. D	27. C	35. D
4. B	12. B	20. B	28. C	36. C
5. A	13. C	21. A	29. A	
6. A	14. A	22. C	30. D	
7. D	15. D	23. C	31. A	
8. B	16. B	24. B	32. B	

Chapter 8

1. A	10. A	19. D	28. A	37. D
2. C	11. C	20. B	29. A	38. D
3. B	12. D	21. C	30. B	39. D
4. A	13. A	22. D	31. C	40. B
5. C	14. B	23. D	32. C	41. D
6. C	15. D	24. D	33. D	42. C
7. D	16. C	25. D	34. A	
8. C	17. A	26. D	35. D	
9. D	18. B	27. C	36. B	

1.	D	16.	A	31.	D	46.	C	61.	C
2.	D	17.	A	32.	A	47.	A	62.	C
3.	A	18.	C	33.	A	48.	C	63.	D
4.	C	19.	A	34.	A	49.	B	64.	A
5.	B	20.	D	35.	D	50.	A	65.	C
6.	D	21.	C	36.	C	51.	A	66.	D
7.	B	22.	A	37.	B	52.	C	67.	D
8.	C	23.	C	38.	C	53.	B	68.	C
9.	B	24.	A	39.	B	54.	A	69.	C
10.	D	25.	B	40.	C	55.	D	70.	D
11.	A	26.	C	41.	C	56.	C	71.	D
12.	A	27.	D	42.	A	57.	B	72.	C
13.	C	28.	B	43.	D	58.	C	73.	C
14.	A	29.	D	44.	C	59.	A	74.	C
15.	D	30.	A	45.	A	60.	B	75.	D

Chapter 10

Firefighter I

1.	A	13.	C	25.	C	37.	A	49.	A
2.	C	14.	D	26.	B	38.	C	50.	A
3.	B	15.	A	27.	B	39.	D	51.	B
4.	B	16.	B	28.	D	40.	B	52.	A
5.	D	17.	D	29.	C	41.	A	53.	A
6.	C	18.	C	30.	D	42.	B	54.	B
7.	A	19.	C	31.	A	43.	D	55.	D
8.	D	20.	D	32.	D	44.	C	56.	A
9.	A	21.	A	33.	C	45.	B		
10.	B	22.	A	34.	A	46.	D		
11.	A	23.	C	35.	B	47.	A		
12.	D	24.	D	36.	B	48.	B		

Answer Key

1. C	11. D	21. A	31. A	41. C
2. C	12. B	22. C	32. B	42. C
3. D	13. A	23. A	33. D	43. D
4. C	14. C	24. B	34. C	44. B
5. D	15. B	25. A	35. B	45. D
6. B	16. C	26. D	36. A	46. C
7. B	17. A	27. D	37. C	47. C
8. B	18. B	28. D	38. B	48. C
9. C	19. C	29. C	39. D	49. C
10. A	20. C	30. A	40. D	50. A

Chapter 12

Firefighter I

1. D	8. A	15. A	22. C	29. A
2. C	9. D	16. B	23. C	30. C
3. A	10. C	17. B	24. B	31. A
4. A	11. B	18. B	25. C	32. D
5. B	12. C	19. D	26. B	33. C
6. A	13. D	20. D	27. A	34. D
7. B	14. C	21. C	28. C	35. C

Chapter 12

Firefighter II

1. A	9. B	17. C	25. C	33. A
2. D	10. C	18. D	26. D	34. B
3. C	11. C	19. A	27. A	35. D
4. B	12. A	20. B	28. B	36. A
5. A	13. A	21. B	29. A	37. C
6. B	14. D	22. B	30. D	
7. A	15. C	23. C	31. C	
8. D	16. A	24. B	32. D	

Answer Key

1. A	13. A	25. D	37. A	49. B
2. A	14. C	26. B	38. C	50. C
3. B	15. B	27. D	39. C	51. A
4. B	16. B	28. A	40. D	52. A
5. B	17. B	29. D	41. A	53. D
6. B	18. A	30. C	42. A	54. B
7. B	19. A	31. A	43. C	55. B
8. B	20. B	32. D	44. A	56. D
9. A	21. B	33. C	45. D	57. B
10. B	22. D	34. D	46. A	58. D
11. B	23. C	35. A	47. B	59. A
12. C	24. C	36. B	48. B	60. A

1. C	8. D	15. C	22. B	29. C
2. A	9. D	16. D	23. A	30. C
3. B	10. B	17. A	24. D	31. C
4. D	11. C	18. D	25. A	32. A
5. C	12. D	19. A	26. B	33. A
6. A	13. B	20. C	27. A	34. A
7. C	14. D	21. D	28. B	

1. D	8. A	15. B	22. B	29. A
2. A	9. D	16. B	23. D	30. D
3. D	10. A	17. B	24. C	31. A
4. C	11. B	18. C	25. D	32. C
5. B	12. B	19. B	26. B	33. C
6. A	13. C	20. A	27. D	34. D
7. A	14. A	21. B	28. C	35. C

Answer Key

Chapter 14

Firefighter II

1. B	10. D	19. A	28. A	37. C
2. A	11. C	20. D	29. D	38. D
3. D	12. A	21. D	30. C	39. A
4. C	13. B	22. C	31. A	40. B
5. D	14. A	23. B	32. C	41. D
6. A	15. B	24. B	33. D	42. D
7. D	16. B	25. B	34. B	
8. D	17. D	26. A	35. A	
9. C	18. B	27. D	36. B	

Chapter 15

Firefighter I

1. C	14. B	27. C	40. A	53. A
2. B	15. C	28. C	41. C	54. A
3. D	16. A	29. A	42. B	55. B
4. C	17. D	30. C	43. C	56. A
5. C	18. D	31. D	44. D	57. C
6. B	19. C	32. A	45. A	58. B
7. C	20. A	33. B	46. C	59. D
8. D	21. D	34. B	47. A	60. C
9. C	22. A	35. D	48. C	61. C
10. D	23. C	36. C	49. B	62. A
11. A	24. C	37. D	50. D	63. B
12. A	25. A	38. A	51. D	64. A
13. B	26. D	39. D	52. B	

Chapter 15

Firefighter II

1. B	8. C	15. D	22. D	29. B
2. D	9. B	16. C	23. C	30. C
3. D	10. A	17. B	24. A	31. B
4. C	11. C	18. C	25. C	32. B
5. D	12. D	19. D	26. A	33. A
6. B	13. D	20. B	27. C	34. C
7. D	14. A	21. D	28. B	35. B

Chapter 16

1. B	8. B	15. D	22. A	29. B
2. D	9. D	16. B	23. A	30. C
3. B	10. D	17. D	24. A	31. C
4. C	11. C	18. D	25. B	32. C
5. B	12. C	19. D	26. C	
6. A	13. A	20. B	27. A	
7. D	14. B	21. B	28. A	

Chapter 16

1. D	13. A	25. B	37. A	49. B
2. D	14. B	26. D	38. D	50. B
3. D	15. A	27. B	39. D	51. A
4. B	16. B	28. A	40. B	52. A
5. B	17. A	29. C	41. D	53. A
6. B	18. B	30. C	42. C	54. B
7. B	19. A	31. B	43. B	55. C
8. A	20. A	32. A	44. A	56. A
9. C	21. B	33. B	45. C	57. A
10. D	22. A	34. B	46. D	58. B
11. C	23. A	35. C	47. B	59. C
12. B	24. C	36. A	48. A	

Chapter 17

1. D	10. D	19. A	28. D	37. C
2. A	11. B	20. A	29. B	38. A
3. B	12. A	21. B	30. D	39. D
4. B	13. D	22. B	31. D	40. A
5. C	14. A	23. B	32. C	41. D
6. D	15. D	24. C	33. D	42. D
7. C	16. B	25. A	34. C	43. D
8. C	17. B	26. B	35. A	44. D
9. A	18. B	27. B	36. A	45. A

Answer Key

1. A	7. A	13. D	19. D	25. B
2. A	8. D	14. D	20. D	26. D
3. B	9. A	15. C	21. B	27. D
4. D	10. A	16. A	22. C	28. A
5. D	11. A	17. A	23. D	
6. D	12. D	18. A	24. B	

1. A	8. A	15. D	22. D	29. A
2. C	9. D	16. B	23. B	30. D
3. B	10. B	17. A	24. B	31. D
4. B	11. D	18. C	25. D	32. C
5. B	12. A	19. C	26. C	
6. D	13. C	20. D	27. C	
7. B	14. A	21. D	28. D	

1. A	9. D	17. A	25. C	33. B
2. D	10. D	18. A	26. C	34. D
3. C	11. A	19. D	27. B	35. C
4. C	12. B	20. D	28. B	36. D
5. D	13. C	21. A	29. A	37. A
6. D	14. A	22. A	30. A	38. D
7. C	15. A	23. B	31. B	39. D
8. B	16. D	24. A	32. A	40. A

1. B	6. A	11. A	16. A	21. A
2. B	7. D	12. D	17. A	22. A
3. A	8. C	13. C	18. D	23. A
4. A	9. A	14. B	19. D	24. A
5. C	10. B	15. D	20. D	25. D

Answer Key

1. A	13. D	25. A	37. B	49. D
2. D	14. A	26. A	38. C	50. D
3. A	15. A	27. B	39. D	51. D
4. B	16. B	28. A	40. A	52. A
5. B	17. B	29. A	41. A	53. D
6. B	18. A	30. B	42. D	54. D
7. B	19. B	31. C	43. D	55. B
8. A	20. C	32. B	44. D	56. A
9. C	21. C	33. D	45. B	57. C
10. D	22. A	34. C	46. A	58. B
11. C	23. A	35. B	47. B	59. B
12. B	24. B	36. B	48. A	60. C

Chapter 21   Firefighter I

1. C	14. D	27. C	40. A	53. D
2. B	15. D	28. C	41. B	54. D
3. D	16. A	29. B	42. A	55. D
4. D	17. A	30. D	43. D	56. B
5. D	18. B	31. A	44. C	57. B
6. C	19. C	32. D	45. A	58. C
7. C	20. C	33. A	46. D	59. D
8. B	21. A	34. A	47. C	60. B
9. D	22. B	35. D	48. A	
10. C	23. B	36. C	49. B	
11. A	24. C	37. A	50. A	
12. A	25. B	38. B	51. C	
13. C	26. D	39. C	52. B	

Answer Key

1. C	16. A	31. A	46. A	61. C
2. A	17. C	32. A	47. B	62. B
3. B	18. A	33. A	48. D	63. A
4. D	19. A	34. B	49. D	64. A
5. B	20. C	35. D	50. C	65. A
6. C	21. D	36. B	51. B	66. A
7. C	22. A	37. B	52. D	67. B
8. B	23. C	38. C	53. B	68. C
9. A	24. B	39. D	54. B	69. B
10. B	25. D	40. A	55. B	70. C
11. B	26. D	41. A	56. B	
12. D	27. D	42. D	57. D	
13. B	28. A	43. B	58. C	
14. A	29. D	44. A	59. A	
15. C	30. A	45. C	60. C	

1. C	13. C	25. B	37. D	49. D
2. A	14. D	26. C	38. D	50. A
3. C	15. C	27. C	39. B	51. C
4. C	16. D	28. B	40. B	52. C
5. C	17. C	29. C	41. B	53. C
6. A	18. C	30. A	42. B	54. B
7. A	19. A	31. A	43. C	55. B
8. A	20. C	32. D	44. A	56. C
9. B	21. B	33. B	45. D	57. B
10. C	22. C	34. C	46. D	58. D
11. B	23. C	35. C	47. D	59. D
12. B	24. C	36. C	48. B	60. C

Answer Key